CHASED BY THE MEMORY

A BOY'S STRUGGLE FOR IDENTITY

CHASED BY THE MEMORY

A BOY'S STRUGGLE FOR IDENTITY

MICHAEL HARTOONIAN

Henschel
HAUS
publishing, inc.
MILWAUKEE, WISCONSIN

HenschelHAUS Publishing, Inc.
Milwaukee, WI 53220
www.henschelHAUSbooks.com

HenschelHAUS books may be purchased for educational, business, or sales promotional use. For information, please email info@henschelHAUSbooks.com

ISBN: 978159598-540-8
E-ISBN: 978159598-541-5
LCCN: 2018958426

For
Cricket, Linc, Kate, Emily, Hannah, Keaton,
Brandon, Henry, Grant, Pip, Cam, and Martin

ACKNOWLEDGMENTS

I WOULD LIKE TO THANK THE FOLLOWING friends for encouragement, critical reading, and conversations about the content and style of the narrative: Alice Thornton, Linda Canfield, Todd Beach, DeAn Krey, Richard Van Scotter, Stanley Trollip, and Walter Hartoonian. And, to my wife, Patty Thornton, for hours of editing and her persistent question, "Is this really what you mean to say?!"

THANK YOU, MAMA *

With the intangibles of genes, enzymes, and environments,
You gave me life and placed me in a web of love.

With bread and milk and grace,
You taught me to predict the weather of my soul.

With wonder and song,
You set me on a journey through the firmament of time.

With uncommon vision,
You helped me understand proper service.

With exceptional courage,
You turned me to search the skies and to find myself.

Thank you, Mama,
For providing the seedbed, the love, the music, and courage.

For Birth.

—Michael Hartoonian

* For Patricia Schnobrich, 2014

PREFACE

THESE ARE THE REFLECTIONS OF AN ELDERLY man as he looks back at his four years in high school. It is a personal story about an uprooted Chicago boy transplanted to the small, culturally and religiously isolated town of New Kassel in northeastern Wisconsin. The story centers on the distorted role of athletics in the minds of young men in small-town America in the 1950s, and on their gender and race unconsciousness. At age seventeen, this boy was athletic enough to earn the golden prize coveted by almost every boy, a try-out with a major league baseball team.

However, the story is primarily about the ongoing philosophical search for family and love, and the inner arguments about the human desire to connect to something, even to the land. It reveals the blind faith of the family farmer of the 1950s, with no lifeline to the government or to a corporation.

Above all, this is an investigation of the ethical and physical lessons that an elderly person can learn by paying attention to his childhood. It is an inquiry into the values and tensions that we have confronted and incorporated into the creation of our character. Three unanswerable questions guide the narrative:

- *What happens to a boy who is forced to compete for the smallest bits of emotional and material security?*
- *Who do you become when you believe that no one cares about you?*
- *Can you build a life without being a loving critic of your own life?*

Names and identifying details of people and places mentioned in the book have been changed for stylistic reasons and to respect privacy. The story, while set in a real place and time, portrays both fictitious and real composite events and people.

In remembering,
we free ourselves from the past.

Michael Hartoonian
Saint Paul, MN

1

TEN O'CLOCK. THE ROOM WAS COMPLETELY DARK. The last candle had gone out some thirty minutes earlier. Outside the window, the fields and woods beyond pose a threatening mystery. Through the open window, a damp and pungent farm breeze carries an odor of sadness that, to this day, I can ride back to that long-ago night in that unfamiliar room.

Even before the first hint of morning light, some cheerful sparrows and a chorus of far-off quail interrupt a deep sleep. A new day and a new life now force their way into my consciousness, breaking the sequence of a dream and creating a new memory, one that still chases me some sixty-plus years later.

I have spent decades since that night. How well the time has been spent is an open question. Perhaps they are wise who have discovered that the most pleasant time is understated. It is the time without arrogance, without victory, and without material value. Travel widely, say little, and understand that meaning, and perhaps even happiness, are possible only through a covenant with restraint—a life of happy simplicity.

So here I am, sixty years after that first night, restraint on my mind, driving by chance on the road that leads to the old house and farm, my sight dimmed by an avalanche of memories. I am passing through a quiet autumn landscape, going to see an ill boyhood friend. This is the place in which I grew to adulthood, or at least to the age of majority; the place that defined the reliability of friendship. Dominant in my memory, however, is Mama, or Rose, with her food and pleasing smile.

The heart-whirling anticipation I once felt as an adolescent moving down this road overtakes me. Mama, Happy, Mark, and even my landscape are all gone now. I know that. That's a fact, but it's not the truth. Today there is an empty feeling that I know won't be filled by reaching a destination. This landscape I once saw as a sensuous vitality, seems now to be dying from an exquisite apathy.

This is small-family-farm country in northeastern Wisconsin. For almost eighty miles directly west of Green Bay, perhaps an area of 6,000 square miles, is a region blessed with hard land and poor people. "If rocks were pennies, I'd be a millionaire," still is the common complaint around here. We had more than our fair share of stones, put in place by the Wisconsin Glacier that covered much of central and northeastern North America some twenty-two thousand years ago.

The receding glacier created a topography where it was often possible to walk on rocks across a cow pasture without touching any soil. While the land gave a unique sense of being hard, cold, and forbidding to the enormous machines found on the larger farms in the southern parts of the state, I never saw the same hardness reflected in the souls of the people who produced a cultural harvest as rich as any I have known. I worked this land and lived with these people so I saw inside both. From inside, the view is always different—more complex, mysterious, and comforting than the picture presented when only seen from inside a car moving at 70 miles per hour on Highway 29 or Highway 45.

We grew hay, oats, some corn, and a vegetable garden in that order, but the cows always came first. We raised some hogs and chickens, had three horses. But cows—milk, butter, and cheese—those were the prizes. In most years the mortgage outgrew our crops, our cows, and even our relationship to the land. Some of what we built and planted, like stone fences and trees, has outlasted the six decades since, but for the most part, we left no trace of passing. In the end, it's not the farmer, nor the cows, nor even the lending banks—it's the memory that survives.

All roads home are hauntingly familiar. As I pass over the small Embarrass River, I remember diving from this bridge as a teenager and fishing here too, always with friends. Few are left. War, age, work, and even deer hunting have taken their tolls. The road looks so narrow and the bridge so old. The thought of diving down to the water now frightens me. In those days I was afraid of nothing—with the possible exceptions of Mama and some of my teachers.

Teachers frightened me because I thought they held the keys to the future, and I wasn't clear on how to access that domain. I think I'm still trying to access it. Mama frightened me because I never knew where she would be in place, in time, or in mind. I had an inconsistent sense of her love for me. She was, I think even then, a memory, a remembrance devoid of facts, an intuition. But that is the case with all things dear, loved, reviled, or hated. Thinking about and judging those who are significant to you always leads to the truth that believing is seeing, and not the other way around.

The important things in life—things like God, love, mar-riage, jobs, spouse, kids, teachers, war, elections, and, of course, Mama—are all about belief. You see what you want to see because of what it says about you to others. The presidential candidate, the teacher, the child, the spouse, even the church attended, are all about us and our relationships; beliefs color these "realities" to our advantage. We would like to believe that we are confident in our knowledge of the facts as well as our personal judgments, rebellious against any authority, skeptical about orthodoxies of all types, and responsible for our own actions. These may be our dreams, not what is real.

We remember with a sense of advantage. The older I get, the better I was.

The relationship between reality and truth is not unlike the relationship between sex and love, or technique and artistry. Sometimes we use those words interchangeably, but there is a world of difference between them. Perhaps, in the end, the best we can say is that life is random, and we are so anxious about uncertainties that we hang our decisions and behaviors on worldviews devoid of any coherent or rational notion of the world. We should, however, also beware of our beliefs, which are in themselves creatures of randomness.

Crossing over the river, the road, now in deep and vibrant shadows, is still recognizable. The trees along the side are much larger. The county has tried to straighten the old road here and there leaving a green and overgrown corridor through the woods where the "old road" ran before. While the straightened seg-ments of the road seem a little wider, it looks out of place and much less inviting. The trees used to come right up to the old road forming a canopy that sheltered the path and made travel cool even on the hottest summer day. Today only weeds and some berry bushes come near making the drive hot and dusty and almost barren.

Roads, perhaps like people, have to be careful about the possibility of being empty as they focus on destination and attempt to cross distances in straight lines. For the most part, though, the road still meanders toward the old farm. I know, of course, that Mama is gone and the thought breaks my concentration from the landscape. I am rushed away with a flood of feelings and my tears feed the melancholy that is the material of which memories are made, but always left unfinished. We have little control over which memories we remember. Memories have control of memories. How I wish that I could drive up around the old yard-light pole, rush into the house, throw my arms around her, spin her around the kitchen and wait not more than ten seconds for her perpetual first question: "Are you hungry?"

I am hungry, Mama. Hungrier than ever, for your food and love, but also for life, for my identity, and to understand who you were and still are to me. I don't believe that I ever knew you. I don't even know why I should love you if, in fact, I do. So why now, after all these years, do I want to talk to you about your understanding of joy, and the ability to withstand one disaster after another—you, who outlived three husbands, and experienced the Great Depression, World War II, prejudice, the death of your child, and the work, work, work. I would like to know who I was to you. What did I mean to you? Did you love me? You never said so. Your door and your heart seemed open to others and, when you died, I wanted to believe that the world became a little colder and a little less friendly. But was that a wish or the truth? Anyway, it's good to remember you, particularly in this landscape, and if I can, I may yet create the foundation of my identity and understand the nature of your life's web.

Wiping away another tear, my memory is in full control.

The first time I traveled this old road was not the late autumn of my reverie, but early spring. I was thirteen. The gravel road was wet with deep ruts made from milk trucks, tractors, and the few visitors who passed this way. I remember the cool spring air filled with farm odors. The dirty snowbanks along the road were still bright in the warm spring sunlight, and they produced such a volume of snowmelt that the ditches on either side of the road were little rivers, with branches and some oak leaves playing the role of ships.

Mostly, I remember the smell—the pungent odor of wet grass, cow manure, and clear, cool air in the dairy land of northeastern Wisconsin. The smell of that day is a sensory touchstone to which I can return at will. The wafting odor of fresh hay stacked in the barn evokes times of flirting with local girls as well as flirting with injury or death. Life, love, death all blended together in the scent of memory.

2

THE BLACK 1936 FORD WAS SPOTLESS, inside and out. This was our "magic carpet" to the future. That was Mama's take on it. We left our home on Lawndale Street in Chicago at four in the morning and now in the early afternoon, were arriving in Fairbanks Township to take up a new life. Mama's friend, Buzz, drove us up north, a two-wheeled trailer crammed with all our stuff in tow, and deposited my mother, my younger brother Mark, and me. We were about to meet our new stepfather and be introduced to a new land.

"New land, hell," I thought, "what about the Chicago-land that I was leaving?" Less than a week previous, and in a matter of days, the commanding tones of motherhood told us to leave friends and teammates and our diverse, dynamic, and poor urban landscape of childhood.

From the time I was five or six, I saw Chicago as a marvelous world. The streets, alleys, and rooftops seemed an ideal context in which to fight dragons, hide from monsters, and explore far-off places and times. As I grew into early adolescence, I gained respect from my peers and adults alike, becoming a good athlete and leader of my own little multi-ethnic group of wise-guys. We were free to travel the city on foot and by streetcar. Kids like us had the full run of the city in those days. Parents either cared enough or not enough to let us explore, as long as their will was obeyed. We all knew the sanctions imposed when that will was violated.

Then, out of the clear blue, my mother made the pronouncement; "We're moving to a farm in Wisconsin." I knew nothing of the man who would come to be our father. Mama had only married him one month before. And she hadn't said a word about the marriage or the man she married until that day. I would be graduating from Ryerson Elementary in June and several high schools were interested in having me play ball for them in the fall. In early March, I was on top of the world. But that was not what she saw in my future. And what she saw was what we all would come to see.

My biological dad had died and my persistent fear was that no one would remember him. He would just disappear. The fear of death is nothing compared to the fear of disappearing. Perhaps, it's a case of geography; at least the dead have a unique or special imaginary location. I was seven when my father died—disappeared. No one was sure of the cause of death. "A stomach problem," was the best I could ever get, even from Mama.

He had married Mama in the late 1930s. She had been married before. Her first husband died in 1923, leaving her with three young children to bring up. By the time Mark and I came along, they were all young adults living on their own and displayed little thought for their mother or two step-brothers. Less than a year after my dad's death, our lack of income forced us to move out of our walkup flat on Noble Street.

I loved my life on Noble Street. The flat, which took up the whole third floor of the four-story brick tenement building, had six rooms—three small bedrooms, kitchen, living room, dining room, and a bathroom off the kitchen. The front door opened off the dining room onto a dimly lit stairway with hardwood floors that responded fondly to anyone walking or running up or down the stairs. Off the kitchen, open wooden stairs led down to the alley and basement where dirty coal bins dominated an already dark environment.

Basements continue to be a source of discomfort for me. After Dad's death, I had to go down and bring up a bucket of coal every night in the dead of winter. There was no central heat and we used the coal for heating, cooking, and for warming water for baths. We had a large space-heating stove in the dining room and a cook stove in the kitchen. In the winters, smoke from coal fires turned the skies dirty—so dirty that on many days the clothes that Mama hung out to dry on lines strung between tenements returned covered with specks of soot.

The Novak family, who lived on the fourth floor, had seven children; the Newmanns on the second floor had three, and then there were my brother and me on the third floor. The smells of cooking and noise of children always filled the hallways and stairs.

The first floor housed a small grocery store where they also baked bread and cakes. The owner, Mr. Hofmann, lived behind the store with his wife and their two sons. A block away stood a large Catholic church, and the park beyond provided a great place to play games of all kinds, including softball. A drugstore with a wonderfully stocked candy counter completed our block.

Four blocks away was Peabody Elementary School, which, after the park, was my favorite place in the whole city. I would only finish third grade there because with Dad's death, we had to move to a place we could afford.

What we could afford was a two-room basement apartment with a toilet stool and shower on the other side of the furnace and coal bins, about forty feet from our door, our only door. One room served as a storage room and bedroom for Mark and me and the other room served as the kitchen, dining room, living room, and Mama's bedroom.

We had a portable radio and three or four books—the extent of our home-entertainment center. Our imaginations rode with *The Lone Ranger* and solved mysteries with *The Shadow*. We laughed at Jack Benny, and, best of all, listened to baseball. During the summer, a Cubs game was always on someone's radio. On any warm June day, with windows open and volumes high, I might walk two or three blocks and never miss a play.

As often as we could, we went to Wrigley Field, the Cubs Park. We would save up the 50-cent admission price or, most of the time, just sneak in. The Brooklyn Dodgers were my team, and PeeWee Reese my player. I saw him play several times at Wrigley. By the time I was in eighth grade, I was about his size and could imagine playing his position. I intentionally developed my skills as a player and as a gentle athlete to reflect the player that PeeWee was. I loved the story of how he stood up for Jackie Robinson, the first black player in the big leagues, whose baseball skills and human strength seemed beyond attainment and almost god-like. Although not as strong as Jackie, PeeWee was a gentleman who could play and lead with the best of them and I wanted to be like him.

Watching baseball was a magical pastime, and we watched them all—the Cubs, St. Louis, Pittsburgh, and the New York Giants. But the Dodgers with Robinson, Roy Campanella, Duke Snider, Gil Hodges, Carl Erskine, Joe Black, and Don Newcombe, perhaps, the largest man I had ever seen in my young life were the best. All played right in front of me.

We would get to the park before batting practice. I loved to watch the pepper games played outside the first and third foul lines, and guys hitting fungos to outfielders, so high the balls seemed to disappear in the clouds. And we would never miss the teams taking infield. My eyes stayed glued to Reese or whoever was playing shortstop. I would watch and practice all the next weeks and months of summer to become "good." Playing the infield was one continuous act of artistry. Playing shortstop, I loved the feel of a hot grounder off the short hop and making the throw to first in one motion. And, coming across second base to complete the double play was pure poetry.

To me, at that time, and for some time to come, baseball seemed like the truth—simple and freeing. On the field, we had democracy. You were judged by your actions, right there; parents didn't matter, money didn't matter, color and religion didn't matter, at least to us kids.

Movies! We also spent at least one day a week at the movies—twelve cents a show—a sum that we earned by collecting bottles and cans and selling them to our "junkman," who roamed the alleys around our apartment in his cart, pulled by the oldest horse I had ever seen. He would shout out some unintelligible words that sounded like "rags-a-line," perhaps, "rags and iron," and people would magically appear bringing out their junk—

papers, iron and tin, glass, and rags. Maybe we already had a kind of recycling and just didn't know it. Whenever we needed twelve cents, we could always count on the junkman.

I especially remember the hot, hot, August afternoons—evenings, too, when we would sit and often sleep on someone's fire escape—but, mostly, on the hottest of days, we would walk to the movies. The theaters were the only places in the neighborhood that had air conditioning! The "Air-Conditioned Comfort" sign was prominent on the marquee. To this day, theaters have a feeling and smell all their own, especially in the summer.

If we got in by two in the afternoon, we could see two feature movies, two cartoons, a newsreel, and two or three serials. And, it would still be light outside when we left, sometimes so light it would hurt your eyes, as reality does when returning from a dream.

We loved Superman, Flash Gordon, and Red Ryder and Little Beaver, among others. The theater provided beautiful brochures with previews of coming attractions for the next week, and we could use them for planning our week's activities or for making paper airplanes. Mostly, we did the latter. Movies defined our summer afternoons—popcorn, romance, adventure, and all in a cool place.

Years later, my brother and I agreed that given the environment in which we grew up, we probably received our foundational values from the Big Screen in a time when movies tended to present more simplistic statements about right and wrong, but didn't present women or minorities as capable people. That would hurt us later.

Movie narratives and ballgames taught me much about archetypal life, but not so much about real life. There was no mentor, no advisor, no one to help reflect on the triviality of hitting a baseball. There simply was no constant adult in our lives. My mother worked two jobs: one at Motorola, the other selling hot dogs in the summers, first on the corner of Milwaukee Avenue and Noble Street, and then at Chicago and Lawndale Avenues.

From Memorial Day to Labor Day, from about six p.m. to midnight, she was gone. This left us free to explore at will, while Mama thought we were in bed. Mark and I flirted with trouble, but we could run and hide with the best and needed to answer to no one but ourselves—and Mama, if she caught us.

I was on my own from the time I was eight and liked it. In Chicago, I had an identity; I knew I was somebody. Somebody who, by the sixth grade, could hit a home run, or throw a touchdown pass almost anytime I wanted to, or shoot marbles better than anyone on the block, or run the fastest from the pursuing guards in the Field Museum; guards who could never catch me. I was also the one who caught grass snakes in Chicago's forest preserves and freed them in the neighborhood Catholic Church and in the swimming pool across the street from the church, just to scare people and to see if snakes could swim. They can.

And yet, I was praised by my teachers for scholarship and citizenship. When I told Miss Sullivan that we were moving to Wisconsin that March, the school gave me a "free ride" through April and May, and promised that, though absent, my name would be listed as a graduate when the rest of my eighth-grade class finished in June. My hours in school were the times when my life felt certain. I secretly had hoped that she'd insist I stay to finish the year.

Half the time, I didn't know Mama's whereabouts. Meals were not very regular and the days had few time markers, except for the radio programs we listened to in the evening. From time to time, Mama would bring a man "friend" home, and we would fall asleep in the kitchen, often listening to the sounds of "love" coming from our room. On those nights, I often woke up, feeling afraid, and getting my brother up so we could go for a walk, sometimes on cold winter nights. I made Mark come with me because I didn't want to walk the dark streets alone in those early hours. And I didn't want to be in that basement apartment either. At those times, my imagination could find no place else for me to be. I still don't know if those experiences made me feel happy or sad for Mama. My hunch is that she wanted to end this kind of life and Wisconsin was her answer.

Mama had been born in Italy to a family with agricultural roots. She came to America as a child of six as the 20th century opened. Ellis Island was her welcoming port and she and her family waited on the wrong side of the gates for several days because her sister was detained due to a fever. After a week or two in New York, the Alberti family moved to Chicago, where her father had relatives.

My father's story is similar. His parents were also farmers whose origins were near the Black Sea in the region now known as Georgia. Just prior to the Armenian genocide, his older brother took him to France and through a roundabout way, my father eventually ended up in America. The Hartoonian family also had relatives in Chicago, and at age 16, my father also found himself in the Windy City living with an aunt and uncle from the same Black Sea region. I grew up with Armenian pride and the aroma of Italian food.

I loved the food Mama and my friends' mothers and some of the dads cooked. Peasant food recipes brought from the old country as they called and recalled their places of birth. Peasant food is the best food because cooking potatoes twenty different ways demands creativity. Most of the parents gave us wine to drink with our meals—an inch of wine in the bottom of a large glass topped to the brim with water.

The adults talked about food in relationship to the functions of the body. Onions and tomatoes were good for your skin and digestion; buckwheat and coffee were good for your heart; cheese and wine were good for your soul; and fish and garlic were good for almost everything, particularly sex. When you're poor, sex seems everywhere before you. That is probably why the sweet smell of sautéing garlic still brings backs so many memories—they all used a great deal of it.

All this folklore about garlic and wine hid a deep ambivalence and anger about my childhood and identity that's been an ongoing struggle. The contradictions are poignant. These contradictions started when I was about eight or nine, around the time I began to see how others with more means lived. I came to understand then how poverty and ignorance can define you. I wanted to be nothing like this place.

While I sometimes look back and say it was a great place of ethnic diversity in food and language, in reality, my neighborhood was a place of pain and discrimination. Though I could not articulate it, I began to understand this early. My problem was I had no concept of the good family and the good person, so I tried to achieve a made-up ideal.

But I couldn't trust myself. I didn't have enough knowledge to create a happy reality. This I knew. I knew that being "ethnic" was a roadblock to the world I thought I wanted so I tried to diminish my ethnicity through denial. In the deepest recesses of my mind, I would ironically hold proudly to being Armenian while denying that same identity to the world.

My third-grade teacher, Miss Paulson, whom I adored, often said that she couldn't understand her students. Why didn't we comprehend "common" things and words such as hygiene, concentration, patience, library, health, government … it was a long list. Further, we talked with an "immigrant" sound or accent. I still liked her and what she represented. As I look back, I believe she knew that our language patterns were different from the right patterns and therefore we could not read or write, in the RIGHT way. Too many "foreign" words came out of our mouths and the alignment of verbs in our sentences didn't always match the Standard English patterns.

Listening to Miss Paulson, I often felt ashamed and aware that I was without the privileges she seemed to have—speech patterns, nice shoes, a certain walk. On the other hand, I thought I was learning things. I thought she liked me so why the disparagements from this person I looked up to?

If I wanted to succeed, I would have to be somewhere else and become someone else. That's what I must have thought, even then. My family and culture were out of step with the people who ran the world, and I wanted to be in that other group—not the one I was in. Maybe Mama thought the same.

In that school, in that world, we were all poor, ill-fed, ill-dressed, and often just ill. The adults, with great pride and sadness, talked about the "Old Country," but wouldn't let their kids speak anything but English even though we understood their languages, or at least some of the words. They said, with thick foreign accents, that if you can't speak English with clarity, you'll be considered stupid.

I believe that many immigrants did feel insane in this land that didn't understand them or their stories. Insanity can also be an inability to understand cultural clues. Many had no clue … just work.

There were no books at home to help, no discussions about "the world," no level of expectation except some unreal assumption that, "you could be anything you wanted." I took that to heart, but I also understood that if I really wanted to achieve in school and open the doors that would let me get out, I would also have to leave my family and its culture. I knew that much. So, I did leave. I began to create new places of the mind. My hunch was that Mama also thought of Wisconsin as a new place and a new peace of mind. She saw children not much older than I sent off to jail, killed in street fights, and old in the ways of the world by the time they were twenty. And, these were kids who were smart. Of course, IQ doesn't mean a hell of a lot if no one is talking to you about relationships, and if you don't know where your next meal is coming from.

If I wanted to make something of myself, I innocently believed that first of all, I would have to be a person without my family and without my neighborhood. I would have to invent a new world. If I wanted to leave this place, I would have to become like my teacher—a middle-class, educated, and well-spoken individual who could tell interesting stories about an imaginary family and an imaginary life.

While others invent or reinvent their parents at a much older age, when I was nine, I had already invented a father. He was big and strong, a war hero, gentle, and very smart. These were lies that I told myself until they became real. Then I told others, particularly people important to me. They of course would create images of me based on my created stories of my father. It all added to my fantastical new sense of self.

Truth or reputation? Reputation, of course. With no one to explain the difference, I believed this was the only way. It never really worked. Parts of the old me became very much a part of the new me. In the end, it all turned out to be a whirling mix of cultures and identities that was not much of anything.

My mother was complicit in this denial. She told me almost nothing about my family, her past, her hopes, or her fears. I filled in the historical and emotional gaps. In some respects, the denial worked. Without guidance, I became a person who was sad about the family he didn't have, but had no conception of how to build a new one.

There are, of course, many people who are successful professionals and also never had the security that comes with family. Perhaps those individuals were just born in a better place, at a better time, had better connections, had people to talk to, and were better at staying in one place. Or, perhaps they invented better families or never gave the matter much thought in the first place. For me, it took a long time to understand and get over the resentment that comes when you feel that you are less than others. I began to see the myths created by others regarding their families, as well as the pride therein. To compensate, I developed a fictional pride in my father that was tied to pride in my abilities and my home—Chicago.

I loved Chicago and its common public places that transcended the petty ethnicity of my neighborhood. I loved the museums, the parks, the zoos, the tall buildings, the large department stores, the streetcars, and our ball fields—the streets. And I could "own" it all.

And best of all was Chicago's Maxwell Street where we bought our school clothes each year. One pair of shoes, two shirts, two pants, one coat, some long underwear—that was it. At Christmas, we usually received only one present to supplement our school clothes halfway through the year—one year, a shirt, the next year, a sweater, and on a great year, a book or some game was added. My very best present was the baseball glove that was under our four-foot tree the year I turned eleven. The mitt meant my horizons could be expanded as I could play baseball in other Chicago parks instead of just softball in my neighborhood park.

I was a Chicago kid. I was in the city and the city was in me. My pride in the city seemed to be a reflection of a growing pride in what I could do and what I could be. Yet my love for the city notwithstanding, we moved.

"Ma. What about playing ball in high school? What about my friends? What about my life?"

"Get over it. Be grateful," she said, and nothing more.

3

THERE'S A HIDDEN STORY IN OUR MOVE from the depths of Chicago to the expanse of the farm, a story known only to Mama and Happy, my mother's new husband. Even as an adult, when asked to explain this abrupt and unlikely change, I have to rely on a best guess. I was never told how they came to know each other, but I developed a theory. My father and my father's brother loved to go deer hunting. Happy also loved to hunt. They somehow met in Wisconsin, no doubt in a tavern. Living in Chicago, my dad's best opportunity for such activity was in this part of Wisconsin where he already knew people from vacation trips he and Mama had taken before the war.

The move to the farm threatened to remove my father from my life forever. I worked to maintain my memories of him. Looking back, some are real, and some are fanciful, but it's what I have, and I clung to them. As a young boy, I remember his rifle and shotgun, and particularly the smell of the gun, oil, and cleaning equipment. He owned a pump-action twelve-gauge shotgun, with red paper shells and a .30 caliber rifle with two boxes of golden shells all neatly placed in the deepest, darkest part of my mother's closet. Once I found their hiding place, I would periodically take them out and pretend to hunt or play war games. I always carefully returned the weapons to their original and exact locations.

Other than watching him shave and read the newspaper, I remember very little of my father in my day-to-day life. He seemed big to me, perhaps as all fathers seem to five- or six-year-olds. He would be dead in two years, but I do remember swimming in Lake Michigan with him. We often went to the North Avenue Beach, and he took me for a ride on his shoulders for what seemed like a mile out into the lake. He loved the water. I couldn't wait to return to the beach.

My father worked in one of the ironworks foundries between Chicago and Gary, Indiana, and even drove a cab from time to time. Like many men who worked in the foundries, he was too old for the draft. In 1944, he developed stomach problems—a gallbladder infection, I think—and died. One day, he was just gone.

I knew even less about his early life. He was born in 1900 along the eastern shore of the Black Sea; in the distance, he could see the outlines of the Caucasus Mountains. He would talk about soil, mountains, crops, and even the sea. He said that as a small boy, he lived on a farm, but the farm was taken by Turkish soldiers, and this family fled south and east to escape being jailed or worse. Walking to the store, my five-year-old hand encased by his very big, rough hand or just holding onto his finger, he talked and I imagined pictures from his boyhood. My guess is that he would have loved to be a farmer, but that could never happen. I have assumptions about his childhood and early adulthood but no information. I believe that he was a shy boy, in love with the land and landscape. Years later, my uncle would tell me that he liked to eat soil. I remember thinking, "That's bizarre." I think that Dad was smart, but was always under the influence of his older brother.

I do know that his parents, my grandparents, were killed in 1914 during the Armenian Genocide. With some luck, determination, and great hardship just three years before their parents were murdered, my dad, his brother, Vartin, and their sister, Lalasa, all made their way through Marseille to Paris. Lalasa remained in Paris until her death in 1957. Vartin, who to me was just Uncle for the rest of his life set about getting my dad and himself to America. Immigration records show that my father Mesrop Hartoonian entered the United States under the name of Harbin Mesraartanian, sailing from Khristiania (now Oslo), Norway to Philadelphia. At the time, purchasing other refugee's tickets was sometimes done within ethnic communities. Thus, the ticket bore someone else's name. Presumably, Uncle Vartin bought the ticket and a train voucher for his younger brother and put him on a train toward Kristiania. He then returned to Armenia to find that his parents had been murdered.

At age 17, my father traveled alone from Norway to Chicago and lived with relatives there until he could find a job and support himself. As a young adult, I did meet that cousin, Leo, and two of his children, Bill and Sam. Leo and his wife Ruth had little or nothing to say about my dad. We talked some, but only about the contemporary world and the way it was changing. Life was difficult for my dad and for all those refugees, as it is now for all those who make it to America's borders hoping to escape war, poverty, and violence and make a better life—they must navigate a new landscape, living with new families, doing "city" work, and learning a new language. Yet, they would have said, "Thank God, we got out of the Old Country."

Mama's family came to the United States from Italy in 1906. She was six years old. While her father, Michael, remained in Italy for another two years, she, her mother, sister, and brother arrived in America with ten dollars to their name and an address in Chicago, as reported in the interview questions at Ellis Island. They settled in a small German-Jewish neighborhood on the near northwest side of Chicago's Loop. There, in Chicago, Dad met and married my mother in the late-1930s. She had been married before to an Italian immigrant who died from TB or some respiratory weakness. When she and dad married, Mama brought three adult children from her first marriage to the new family– my, to be, step- sister, and two step-brothers.

My mother's relationship with Uncle Vartin always seemed full of tension. He was mistrustful of others, even his sister-in-law. What worried Uncle, particularly after my father's death, were issues of Armenian traditions. Would his nephews find courage and optimism in the simple stories Mama told and, more to the point, in the life she would live with her boys? Would they learn the long and complex traditions of an ancient people? Would they know about the people who established the first Christian church in the world? Would they learn the unique and singular language that is Armenian? For reasons best known to the displaced or the immigrant, these questions troubled him, and he set out to ensure the answers.

Uncle Vartin. First of all, and last of all, he was Armenian. He wore his nationality openly and with pride. To Uncle, being Armenian was the best fate that could befall one. I later wondered what it must have been like to be a young man concerned with the safety of parents and contemplating a move to a new world. It was a time of suffering in Armenia, a time of fear He returned to Armenia, too late. His parents were dead. I often wondered why he came to Chicago. Why didn't he stay in Paris with his sister? Why his love of Russia and the Czar? Why his hatred of the Bolsheviks and Communists?

He was at a great disadvantage in America. He had a shaky command of English; he was in a culture that he didn't understand, and he was stubborn. In addition, he was big. In the 1940s, at about six-foot four and a muscular 230 pounds, he just seemed out of place. And, he was not friendly. I believed he created complex stories about his origins simply to remain sane, perhaps thinking it possible to keep some sense of sanity by filling his head with old stories. But these stories only separated him more.

I bought into many of Uncle's stories because they were interesting. The stories caused some fuzzy thinking regarding the line between his stories and my feelings toward other people. Unable to express those feelings, I had difficulty thinking about how I fit into the real world, because the stories he told presented people, events, and deeds I didn't see around me.

My grandparents had been murdered by Turkish soldiers. They paid a high price for being Christians. My grandparents were not alone. The record is clear that between 1895 and 1919, the Turks killed, raped, and enslaved over a million people, reducing the percentage of Christians in the region from twenty to two. So Uncle wanted to fight against the Turkish army. To accomplish this, he volunteered as a mercenary in the Russian Army of Czar Nicholas II. His love of Russia was, no doubt, rooted in the context of Europe prior to World War I and the fact that by 1914 the Czar was at war with the Turkish or Ottoman Empire. He sometimes talked about the greatness of Russia and spoke its language fluently. He spoke five languages: Armenian, Russian, German, French, and English. He spoke English with a thick Eastern European accent.

By 1917, as the Bolshevik Revolution reached its apex, he was able to leave, or should I say, escape, Russia. With only the clothes on his back, he lived rough, stealing food and necessities simply to stay alive. Over the next year or so, he made his way back across Eastern Europe, Germany, and France, on his way to England and then sailed from Liverpool to Philadelphia. He arrived in America just before America entered WWI and, after spending time in Philadelphia and New York, he moved to Chicago sometime before WWII to reunite with his brother.

He was only a peripheral part of our lives until he began to insert himself after my father's death. Thinking back, I remember his presence: big, well-dressed, and handsome, but a little off. He was not like the rest of the men we saw. Looking about forty, though already in his fifties, his speech pattern was painfully "foreign," and I was embarrassed by his accent.

For example, he would say, "swevthart" when he meant "sweater." He often asked me to spell and pronounce words from a newspaper which he always carried with him. His "bigness" frightened me. His very presence seemed to bother others. And, he always carried a gun.

If there was anything I liked about him, and perhaps the only thing I liked about him, were his stories. Whenever he had the chance, he would tell us stories, stories about the olden/

golden days of Armenia when Armenia stretched from the Caucasus through the harsh and beautiful landscapes between the Black and Caspian seas, and embraced all the land down to present-day Istanbul. During the reign of Marcus Aurelius, Rome's major eastern ally was Armenia, which would become the first Christian nation after Rome fell and the Empire's capitol moved to Constantinople—named for the first Christian emperor, Constantine. This was the context for his reality, a reality he would try to teach us through his stories.

The legends he told us were about knights and powerful women, who, hand in hand, would do battle against the forces of evil. These were stories once told to children in Armenia as similar stories were told to all children everywhere. Telling stories is the means by which humans become human. Through our imaginations, we create a subjective reality so we can achieve some sense of meaning in a strident natural or objective reality.

It would seem that the objective world needs to be explained through subjective conversations. When the two elements of reason and observation are in intimate communication with one another, we have a chance for civility and progress. When the two domains are without connection, we disrupt our explorations of truth and remove the fragility of civilization. When only one reality is in control, the gods of envy, greed, war, and ignorance will roam the land and raise havoc, destroying both Art and Reason.

I wonder if Uncle knew this. Through these cultural stories, he tried to teach us about rightful behavior. Through these stories, I gained some perspective on strength, courage, beauty, and the beginnings of an understanding that joy is related to conscience. I even began to look forward to his visits, anticipating the next "installment" of the adventures of Chlovly, (*cha-lov-lee*), whom he said was Armenia's most heroic knight. There were tales of heroines and heroes out of Armenia's past; individuals who were stronger and better; people who were good; people who fought evil, and men and women in search of wisdom. Later, I would learn that the rules of life were embedded in those stories and so too was the idea of immortality. These stories suggested a transcendence of everyday life to a better place. This was easy for a kid to understand because kids don't let the world get in the way. Maybe, Uncle thought that even as a child, if I could understand the strength of Chlovy, perhaps I could understand my life's connections to more important (Armenian) things.

I didn't know it at the time, but the point of these stories was to establish an identification or link with more perfect ideals, ancestors, values, homeland, and character.

This identification with powerful myths was, and is still, a way to get beyond the mundaneness of our puny lives. And since my real life seemed dull compared to Chlovy's, I often blurred lines between pretend and real. The quest that gave purpose to heroes, such as Chlovly, would also give me the courage to become more than the passive learner of these stories. I wanted to become the active link between the past and the future. Uncle, and all those who tell stories become the doers of important work—the work of passing on "the good."

Over the years, I have come to think that the work of identifying and passing on the good should be the first aspiration of being human, particularly since it seems to be necessary for our chances of survival even as a species. But this is such hard work and little rewarded.

Uncle's lifestyle seemed mysterious. He made his money betting on horses, living off women half his age, and playing poker. He lived his life as one with great wealth. In contrast, Mark, Mama, and I seemed to have little or nothing. Uncle simply didn't seem to care about anything but himself, and about how to turn his two nephews into Armenians.

From what I could tell, Uncle Vartin never found a home in America. He had no place, only an imagination. If we live in what we love, does the love precede or follow the place? Why wouldn't I be as happy in Bangkok or Anchorage or Rome as in Saint Paul or Chicago? Perhaps, the reason has something to do with the perception of myself I see reflected in the eyes of others.

With rare exceptions, when I'm away from home, there are few reflections in the eyes of strangers. Our rootedness may be a function of how well we see ourselves in the eyes and thoughts of others, and this happens only when we take the time to get to know the other so we can see things through a similar set of values. This common seeing, this common connection, is the first attribute of home or community. We might ask if the emptiness in the eyes of others is caused by social laziness, a lack of common heritage, or by a diminished common hope for the future?

People like Uncle who migrate to a new place have a great deal of courage. In the new country, Uncle would not abandon his past beliefs; they were sacred. He was trying to say that wisdom comes when we use the past to hold our present selves up for inspection. He believed that only when we see ourselves through the lens of the past can we see the "right" way forward. I think he was only half right. Looking back across generations is a tricky business. We need to hold the past up to contemporary assessments, just as we hold the present up to the standards of the past. He just couldn't accept the present as it was so completely different from his old-world experiences, experiences having little or no agreement with his present situation.

"What's your name?" he'd always ask when he came to visit us after my dad's death. He never got over the concern that his family's traditions would die with his brother if he allowed Mama to have full control of our upbringing. Uncle and Mama never got along. Their different visions of how my brother and I should be reared and educated were always in conflict. What church? What school? Even what food should we eat? Uncle's persistent questions and nudges toward an Armenian lifestyle led Mama to see Happy and Wisconsin as a way out. That's my theory, anyway. It helps me explain how my brother and I ended up on a farm in Wisconsin with a new stepfather.

Mama must have had some rationale for leaving Chicago. Choices always have reasons. But someone else's life choices, even made with reason, can be difficult to understand. In the end, it is hard to trace and place the logic of causes and effects in your life because one little change changes everything. A person, a place, a relationship is all there is, all there was, and all there will be. The profound truth is that location has much to do with destiny. Within a few weeks, from Mama's announcement to the last box packed in the car, my location and relationships were forever altered. At thirteen, I was out of the city but could not relate to the farm. My Chicago sense of place, identity, and controlling family stories produced a confusion for me that lingered for years. What I didn't know at the time was that all of these identity narratives are created out of our imagination to help guide our way; they are often not grounded in real life. My task now was to develop a Wisconsin farm identity. But how?

Without some context of landscape and language, I would be powerless to claim a new reality. If you are dropped into a new place, how can new feelings, words, and logic come to replace older ones? Could I describe the tension between old and new? Reality is as much a matter of language as it is a matter of experimental science. The young have little comprehension when thinking about God, sports, school, friends, and family. Many of the words that we use—*smart, love, beauty, rich, truth*—do not exist in nature. They come from the stories we tell each other. I didn't understand that our conceptions of the world stem from the ways we describe it. Language teaches us that there are truths that cannot be verified and words that seem to have nothing to do with the natural world. Yet those words were the keys to understanding my identity. I could not understand these ideas, of course, until I had the knowledge to do so, and that would be a long time in coming. So I was a pushover for Uncle's stories. And the frameworks they provided made my relationship to the world and my mother more problematic.

Parents and extended family shape the character of children. But if they don't, because of absence or neglect, the vacuum will be filled by someone or something else. Depending on the philosophical bent of the parent, identity can be shaped in two different yet related ways.

There are those who believe that the child at birth is a blank slate tabula rasa. Upon that slate must be written the structures of the culture. These rules and stories are revealed to the child as cultural truths, all in good developmental time.

As the child becomes ready, information and wisdom are given. That is, when is it time to learn about friendships, chores, sex, death, war, or even how the sun gets across the sky. Within this mindset, the child is growing into his or her adulthood by learning and following the rules of the culture. This is what the Greeks called mimesis ... mime or mimic. Everyone is clear about the rules, roles, identity, and sanctions involved. In this philosophical tent, good habits, as Uncle Vartin would say, are the doorway to the temple of reason.

Hard work, of course, was also necessary. Genetics notwithstanding, Uncle was clear that our blank slates needed to be written on by him before others had the chance.

The other pathway to adulthood is to assume that some life traits including gender preference, sexual identity, language, and more are innate in the child, and the child just needs to grow into these aspects. The child, in this case, is like a flower—just let it grow. This was more Mama's take on childrearing. All she needed to do is make sure that we had some food, some safe shelter, some affection, and we would be fine. One profound truth was up against another.

No one instructed me on identity or well-being, so I just instructed myself. I had the fallacious idea that the individual can write upon his or her own blank slate. And, like all "self-made" people, I stopped too soon. From the spring of my thirteenth year, I believed that I had only myself to rely on, and so I became leery of the world. I didn't think that Mama or Uncle or anyone was interested in me or my future. After all, Mama altered my world in the name of love. That is, to move us to Wisconsin and just let the process of growing up instruct us. Uncle simply wanted to tell us what to believe and be done with it.

What theory of child development would our stepfather impose? I had no idea, and still wondered what Happy and Mama had in common.

Happy—his given name was Will—was a pleasant man. He had a great smile, was about six feet tall and 240 pounds, and a pretty good teller of stories himself, particularly when drinking beer—one of his favorite pastimes. When we met on that first day, he was fifty or fifty-one, with thin white hair, and white skin—white as in a cross between snow and lard.

Happy was a little heavy, but the visible strength in his arms and neck evidenced the years of hard work he had done on this farm. One could see how Dad might have enjoyed Happy's company as well as hunting with him. I thought I could, too. Happy also had some toys that were irresistible to a thirteen-year -old. A pickup truck, a tractor, three horses, twenty-four cows, some land and forest or woodlot to hunt in, and a whole new set of stories to learn—unlike Uncle's or even Mama's. But most of all, he had a house—a faded white house, where my brother and I could have our own bedrooms! We had a place of our own, but it came with a high rent.

4

THE HOUSE WAS IN NEED OF EVERYTHING. It had no electricity, no central heat, and no plumbing, just a cistern in the basement, and pump on the kitchen sink. Most of all, the place needed cleaning. One thing I did learn early on was the fact that a person can make a hell of a mess just by living each day, particularly if he is too busy to be concerned with household chores. The kitchen was piled high with dirty dishes from what looked to be a hundred dinners.

My hunch is that Happy had long since given up on the idea that you should eat on a clean plate. Doing just enough to get by seemed to be his guiding principle, one that could be very tempting to a child. In fact, it is the child's way.

The house was off the main gravel road that ran into New Kassel just over three miles to the north. The county was planning to blacktop the road so farmers living here could haul Grade A milk, but that wouldn't happen until late next summer. Without a paved road, all a farmer could sell was Grade B milk at a lower price. Grade B milk could only be used to make cheese. There were three cheese factories within twenty miles of the farm, and two breweries. It was Wisconsin.

From the county road, our driveway ran east about fifty yards, past the house on the north side of the drive, and around the yard light that sat atop a twenty-five-foot pole. Here the driveway made a 180-degree turn back toward the road, back past the house. The barn was about twenty yards southeast of the driveway; the machine shed was at least thirty yards from the driveway to the south. The car garage, chicken coop, corn cribs, and granary all stood to the north and east of the house to complete the farmstead scene.

The house faced west, but the common entrance was the back door on the east side. There were large porches on both the front and back of the house. The front or west porch was screened, but not used, except on hot summer evenings when Mark and I would sleep out there. As you came through the back door, you would enter the large and sunny enclosed east porch where we eventually kept barn clothes and a large freezer. Three doors led from this porch: one, straight ahead, into the kitchen; a second door on the right went down into the basement; and a third door, on the left, was entry into the cold pantry. The kitchen was big, bigger than any I had seen before, and Mama made it even bigger by taking out the wall between the kitchen and the second pantry that separated the kitchen from the dining room. We were left with the cold pantry, large enough for all practical purposes, and a built-in glass cabinet between the kitchen and dining room in which Mama kept her "good" plates and glasses.

Beyond the dining room and to the right was a living room about half the size of the kitchen. The door to the front porch was between the dining and living rooms. There were five doors off the kitchen: one to the back porch; one to the pantry; one to the basement; one large archway into the dining and living rooms;

and a smaller arch into a hallway leading to a large master bedroom that we later reduced in size to accommodate a bathroom.

Halfway down that hallway on the right was a door that led upstairs to four bedrooms, one large, and three of about fifteen-by-ten feet in size. Two were on the west side of the house and two on the east. There was also an attic without any insulation.

Then, there was the basement. Unlike other basements I had known, this basement was actually interesting. The ceiling was about eight feet high, and the floor was just hard dirt. There was a cistern to hold rainwater, and a dark corner to store potatoes, apples, and home-canned fruits and vegetables. The other whole side of the basement was given over to the wood-burning furnace and space to store firewood, about three full cords of it.

Mama made plans to remodel the house at once, but until then, we would carry water, use the outhouse, take baths in the copper bath kettle with water heated on the wood-burning stove or just use the river, and hold on to Mama's hidden promise, "Let's see what the fall will bring."

5

WITH THE NEW INDOOR BATHROOM AND electricity, life felt better, and Mama and Happy seemed to get along fine, at least for two fifty-some-year-olds who came from different worlds. Happy had never been married—a farmer whose likeness defined the word "farmer." He cared for cows and the land; he was a good carpenter, mechanic, and veterinarian; and he liked his beer.

I wanted to dress like him. So, we purchased some overalls, shirt, shoes, and gloves for both Mark and me. As time passed, I acquired a farm jacket and cap. Of it all, I thought that gloves had most to do with being a farmer; they were indispensable to the work. The thought and feeling of wearing leather work gloves were the defining element of a farmer's attire.

By late fall, I would also try my first pair of long johns, but I simply couldn't stand them so even on the coldest days I just wore a pair of jeans and overalls. That's when I understood the beauty of overalls. I think that Mama was fine with the idea of me trying to be, or at least look like, a farmer. I believe that my behavior even brought her closer to Happy because every time the chance presented itself, she would proclaim how the boys loved the farm. "See, they even look like they belong here."

As hard as I tried, the city versus country difference was always present. The differences could be seen in Mama's and

Happy's attire but was highlighted most strikingly in their verbal exchanges. Happy loved sauerkraut and liked to make it in a large earthen crock in the kitchen. As it fermented, it gave off a smell not unlike the ones emanating from the old outhouse that had not yet been torn down. Happy would still use it from time to time. Mama suggested that because of the smell, he should make the sauerkraut outside. "What the hell is this world coming to when you have to make sauerkraut outside and shit in the house?" he replied. In the end, Mama won and Happy took the sauerkraut out to the shed.

The cadence of the farm day soon began to push out my thoughts about Chicago, and my resentment toward Mama began to fade. The thing about resentment though is its propensity to return on the most glorious of days. It's like we make little rooms in our minds—resent rooms—in which we keep our monsters locked up. We may think that they are dead, but they are only asleep, and at the most inappropriate times, awaken and destroy our peace of mind, and sometimes our lives.

Even that summer, when she was a constant presence, I spent so little time with Mama that my knowledge of her identity was still anemic. All I have are random recollections. She seemed like a 1970's hippie living twenty years before her time. She cared little for things, dressed to please herself, and didn't give a thought to what people would think of her. She was proper and irreverent at the same time. She was still strikingly beautiful. In a few old pictures that I saw of her as an eighteen- or twenty-year-old, she was a poster girl for the 1920's "flapper."

I wondered if she danced, sang, loved, and discussed world issues. In her mid-fifties now, she seemed focused inward and reflective, like a person who had secrets and memories and decided to live in them and not here with us. Her acts of discipline toward us were applied randomly.

Randomness is difficult to love, and I had little indication that she loved me, or Mark. If she did, she never acknowledged it. She never once said it. The days were busy, and with all the new activities, I didn't really need to engage with deep personal anxieties, hers or mine. We must have had an understanding: you don't bother me and I won't bother you, and together we'll make it through these days.

6

Cows had to be milked twice a day, at 5:30 a.m. and 5:30 p.m. This was lesson number one. In between milkings, fields needed to be prepared for seeding or sowing, and I would learn a whole new sequence of time, tied to the seasons.

This schedule of natural rhythms would never have occurred to the city boy. The cows had to be kept fresh which meant keeping them pregnant in a way that would ensure their highest milk production. A cow would give birth to a calf and be most productive for about four or five months. At that time, she would be again impregnated by a bull or through artificial insemination which the farmers would joke about, pointing to the irrelevance of the human male animal. In nine months, the cow would give birth to another calf and the cycle would be repeated.

The rotation of the field crops was also sequenced for the sake of the cows and the soil. I began to think about it as the 1/3 – 1/3 – 1/3 solution. In any given year, about one-third of the tillable land would be given over to corn, about one-third to oats, and one-third to hay. After three years in hay or green land, the field would be plowed under and prepared for corn. Because corn takes so many nutrients form the soil, we would only allow one yield year of corn, and the field would be plowed for the planting of oats. At the same time, grass seed of alfalfa, clover, and timothy would be planted with the oats.

After the harvest of the oats in the fall, that field would become the hay field for the next three years. After the three years, we would plow it under and plant corn again. This sequence with cow and field presents only the model and not the size or methods of operation. Nonetheless, the sequence was beneficial to the land and the bottom line.

One of the hardest jobs Mark and I had was trying to learn a new vocabulary for the tasks at hand. We had to learn new concepts regarding animals: heifers, pullets, fresh, in heat, dry, gestation, breading, castration, as well as new words about what the animals ate: hay, grain, silage, whey, and grass. We had to know and live with the machinery and all their parts: carburetors, gears, grease fittings, power takeoff, pistons, tires and wheels. Then there was the language of the land and its soil and how to plow, cultivate, and rotate crops, and the multiplicity of weeds, seeds, contours, and fences.

Perhaps the most interesting vocabulary for me was that of weather. The clouds, the wind, the dew, the sun, and the moon were now part of my awareness, and I delighted in them. The things I began to learn about the relationships among humans, land, and animals became ever more complex and interesting with each passing day. But try as I might to assimilate, my location and these new learnings were not coming together for me to form a new identity. My world, though busy, and even exciting, was still unclear and confusing. I was struggling with the old ghost of identity. I didn't fit. Chicago was no longer me; the farm wasn't me. In my most internal thoughts and daydreams, I relied on the construction of some archetypal character in a medieval novel, which, of course destroyed the meaning of the moment. My mind jumped from such stories to the realities of life on the farm. It's a hell of a thing to see the beauty of a landscape, an animal, or of another person, and not have the competence to embrace that beauty. Hell, indeed.

7

SPRING. I AWAKEN TO MY FIRST SPRING day as a warm breeze stirs the trees outside my window. As the dawn and fog give way to the morning sun, I catch only a hint of the remaining winter. The dark soil and splotches of white snow here and there hold my attention for a moment. I can hear Happy is returning from the barn; milking's done. It's 6:40 and somehow, I feel guilty about not helping him. I am old enough to know that I should help, but I'm not sure why.

This feeling will be the beginning of a habit that is usually spurred by shame, but is usually also in my best interest. Working at keeping the land, the animals, and the family amounts to the practice of stewardship. Stewardship is not about owning; it's about working, making better, and being accountable. There is also truth in the notion that we work harder when we feel that the work is related to some measure of ownership. We believe that if we own something it justifies our work.

I owned nothing. As a child, I understood this. On the other hand, I knew I could own my work and love it as I loved the work of baseball. That kind of ownership made me feel good. People could just see what I did and see a happy kid. This was teenage logic of course because self-ownership and identity are as much an attitude as an activity. The attitude is not so much about what you do, but who you are.

I also believed strongly in the unencumbered self. "Just leave me alone." It's how Mark and I grew up. But any self, by itself, cannot shape its character, or respect limits, or serve a community or family. Any conception of self-arising from one's own feelings or needs, though seemingly in line with the idea of the "worth of the individual," is vacuous and asocial, and will impoverish the human potential. Again, the facts of being alone were beginning to push me in unhealthy directions.

Self-interest is never about self, it is about the relationship between self and public—any public—family, team, country, friend, brother, husband, wife, child. My issue wasn't about the ownership of the farm. It was about my lack of relationship with family, as well as with the land. I thought I had belonged to a "family" in Chicago, but being thrust into the new "Happy-Mama" family, the farm family, I floundered for a foothold, redefining whatever notion of family I once thought I had. I wondered if Mark felt the same. He never said.

"How'd the milking go?" I asked Happy, trying hard to suggest that I was sorry about not coming to the barn. Mama was making breakfast, pretending not to be engaged.

"It was a son-of-a-bitch. We have to get a milking machine; 24 cows are just too many for one person."

Mama's contribution is simple, "There are four of us now, and we'll get a milk machine too."

Thinking a bit, Happy said. "You're a big boy, Mike. Mike was your dad's name, too. I liked him. He was a good friend."

There was something more to Happy than his look or his cows.

"You knew my dad?" I would have liked to talk to Happy right then about his friend Mike, but I would let it go for now. I thought there would be time enough for remembering later.

I was wrong. I never did get any information from Happy about my dad. What I learned about him came from two store clerks with whom he did mutual business while he hunted in the area. These two guys now worked at the grain mill where we took our corn and oats to be ground into cow feed. They talked a bit about drinking with my dad, told stories about hunting, and about the advantages of living in this part of Wisconsin.

"After breakfast, we'll clean the barn. I'll let the cows out. It's a warm day and they need their exercise."

"Where's Mark?" I asked. If we were going to clean the barn, I thought that he should be in on the fun.

The breakfast of eggs, bacon, and fresh bread was great. I had no idea how hungry I was. I would have eaten even more had I known that there would not be many more breakfasts like this.

Within three months, Mama would return to Chicago, and thereafter would become a sojourner in my life. Mark, although two years my junior, would in a year take over the important tasks of meal preparation and director of the house and the house's purse.

Mark finally joined us for breakfast. The meal was sprinkled with little conversation—just strangers' talk. Mostly, we discussed improvements to the house and farm, directed, of course, by Mama.

I was the first to leave the house and consciously stepped into my first Wisconsin spring. I had never experienced such a beautiful morning. The sunlight, warm breeze, the embracing scent of wet fields, cow manure in the barnyard, bacon odors from the kitchen—all came together to pleasantly overwhelm this city boy. And I was out of school. My eighth-grade class back in Chicago would be in class today, but I was graduated and ready for high school in the fall.

The barn was across the driveway separated from the house. The walk from the house to the barn, which I would take thousands of times, went by way of the granary and a large corncrib to the south, then by the milk house, which was like an extension of the barn's foundation. The milk house door was within ten feet of the larger barn door.

Each day, the milk house became the place where the hope of wealth, not profit, would be deposited. I came early to understand that wealth, defined as the desire and ability to create excellence, is the only constant in farming; perhaps in life, too. Profits are so violently tossed about on the vagaries of the market that as a small dairy farmer, you stood naked in front of its overwhelming power. Thus, you learned to look for other sources of stability and meaning.

It was said so often that, "farming is a way of life." "We farm because we love the land." "Farming is the backbone of our country." "You are your own boss." "Where else can you work in the sunshine, and for yourself?" It's always so interesting to see how we all create our own realities. I soon came to understand that all of these expressions were rationalizations for telling the world, and coming to believe it ourselves, that we were not insane, but simply followed a different cadence and were above the gross insults of milk prices that really told us what we were worth. But we also believed in and defended that market with our reason, and sometimes our lives.

Approaching the barn from the milk house, I was struck by the size of the stones that made up the foundation of the barn. The stones were of many colors and were all large. Some stones were bigger than others, but all were big. They were also beautiful— differently colored granites and limestones. When I looked closely at the stones, and let my mind work the while, I could see maps of the world, pictures of animals, and as the stone edges caught the morning light I could even see the movement of time.

The barn seemed so big. It was something like sixty feet wide and maybe one hundred twenty feet long. But the field-stone wall, about four feet thick, just kept my attention as I opened the large outer double doors and proceeded through the second set of doors. This would be the first of many, many, times that I would walk through these doors.

Wisconsin dairy barns, built with fieldstone foundations, always have two sets of double doors—for warmth and insula-tion. Each set has to be double to allow large cows to walk in and out with some ease. Going through the doors of the barn was like going through a tunnel to enter a magic place, a place behind massive doors.

The stones on the inside walls were just as big, but here they were whitewashed and everything was bright and clean. And it didn't smell; if anything, it had a rather pleasant odor. Perhaps this is the case because cows are vegetarians and their breath overcomes whatever comes out the other end.

What does a boy do when asked to clean the barn and is confronted with gutters filled with cow manure? There were gutters on both sides—one about eighty feet, the other maybe forty. Luckily, the cows were outside so I just took the wheelbarrow and a shovel and started.

Within ten minutes, Happy came out to show me the skills of shoveling shit, as he would say, and with the promise of a proper tractor ride, I finished the shoveling, spread the straw bedding, and limed the gutters in thirty-five minutes. I became faster, much faster. This was my first chore as a farmer. I learned that the manure metaphor would serve me well throughout life. Each day, no matter how much shit you shovel, tomorrow there will be just as much to shovel again.

"Ready to look at the fields?"

"Yep," I answer, and run out of the barn.

It's almost nine in the morning now; I stand up on the drawbar of the International-Harvester "C" tractor waiting for Happy to take the driver's seat. There's a single plow sitting behind the tractor unattached and looking the worse for wear. The Farmall C is a relatively small tractor, and we later replaced it with a Super Cub and added an International Harvester "M."

Happy was just weaning himself from using horses. But for me, and for now, the C is enough and when Happy asks if I want to drive, I almost knock him off the tractor as I bounce into the seat. From the high seat of the tractor, the morning has become even more beautiful.

Happy breaks the moment, saying, "Let the clutch out slowly." I think I do, but we jerk ahead and stop, killing the engine. I push in the clutch, start the engine, and let the clutch out again. We jerk again, but finally get rolling with the engine running so slowly it seemed like it wants to just stop on its own. I follow the path along the side of the field and we begin to survey just which fields need attention—plowing, dragging, seeding, and, of course, taking the manure from the barnyard and spreading it on the fields that within a month will be planted in corn.

From that first ride, I began to see land as having a personality determined by the fragile harmonies of the soil mixture, the changing weather patterns, and the farmer's attention to place. These attributes of quality and aesthetics continue to be a haunting evaluative theme for my life's decisions. These patterns that I learned from farming were laying the groundwork for attitudes and values far beyond the acreage being plowed.

8

"Who is that?" I ask, noticing a man walking about fifty yards ahead of us on the edge of the field, and not walking well either. Riding behind me on the tractor's draw bar, Happy's reply is matter-of-fact.

"That's Kurt, Kurt Wolfgang, a prisoner of war. Works here from time to time when he's sober."

"Prisoner of war? What war?" I ask.

"World War Two," he says. "He's from some little burg in Germany, was captured just after D-Day, and ended up in Wisconsin in a camp with other German prisoners of war, with people who could understand his language."

"We had camps here? What camps?" I ask.

"Prisoner-of-war camps." Happy continues like he's talking to himself. "He's an embarrassment. He only works hard when he's not drunk because when he's drunk, he always gets sick and shits his pants. Anyway, I asked him to plow under one of the hay fields that we will be planting corn in soon. He started yesterday and must have finished this morning while I was milking. Without thinking, I gave him a case of beer, and in exchange, he agreed to plow the field. I thought he would drink the beer later, but it looks like the son-of-a-bitch left an empty beer bottle at the end of each furrow, and the furrows are all crooked. The field looks like hell."

"What the hell is going on here?" Happy yelled at Kurt.

But Kurt is in no condition to respond. Happy very seldom got angry, but he did at Kurt. Kurt was a blemish on the landscape, but I came to benefit from his perspective on the world, and his uncontrollable drinking was a lesson to both Mark and me. He would long remind me of the foolishness in thinking that my worldview was like everyone's world view.

We waste much of our life's time trying to make others see the world our way. This seems to be the case not only with people from other cultures, but among people from our own families. Never underestimate the power of a person's viewpoint. Perception and taste always seem to trump reason, just as celebrity trumps hero, just as believing trumps seeing.

Given the celebrations of war in most societies including ours, Kurt might even have been a hero at one time. It would not be much of a leap to see him as such, from a distance, of course. He did take a hero's journey, but without any transcendent purpose, just self-preservation, which, however, can be a strong motivator. Whatever the world thought of Kurt, his history, then and now, was informative.

In the fall, Kurt often took me—and sometimes Mark— hunting. We listened to his life's story. He had been unemployed in 1934, then Hitler, he said, dressed him in a uniform, put him in a tank, and gave him dignity. The price of dignity can be high, I know, but to achieve dignity in Germany in the 1930s meant he had to forfeit his better self and become invisible. He had to hide his face from himself. Where's the dignity in that?

Long, rambling conversations with him revealed that Kurt did go to church, but he had no faith. The church presented itself to him as an institution not unlike the military structure he had known under the Nazis. It would take care of him, or at least his soul—forgive him all his sins—and, as with the army, all he had to do was follow orders. To Kurt, they were both about disciples and discipline.

Kurt didn't use any of the clichés about why the Germans allowed a man like Hitler to become their leader. To Kurt, it was simple. In 1934, when the SS started killing German soldiers, like the Brown Shirts, German people became afraid and just closed their eyes to everything. A peaceful majority is no match for a minority of madmen. In fact, the peaceful and silent majority became irrelevant. And, after all, if Hitler could kill members of the German army, he could kill anyone. When people are without work, when they have nothing to eat, when they think everyone is laughing at them, they do anything. There is no thinking, only feelings, only doing.

The church could forgive him, but he couldn't forgive himself. Eventually, Kurt came to believe that the pain of his existence could not be assuaged through the state or the church, but only through the blind courage he found in beer and more beer. He just did not, could not, think about his identity and for good reason. He gave up on the verb "to be" in favor of being able to do any mindless thing. It didn't occur to him that if he didn't know who he was, he wouldn't give a damn about what he could or might do. The emptiness of his life was like a spiritual vacuum able to be filled with any idea that life might bring his way.

Kurt felt separated, alone, non-obligated—a monster. That's what we do with those who are separated; we turn them into monsters. From Beowulf, to Frankenstein's monster, to immigrants' children, to our present-day prisoners—we turn them into monsters through separation. We make them outcasts. We often do the same to ourselves.

Kurt had little or no moral authority or power. Whatever happened to him had left him graceless. He would not consider the notion that a family or country could accept him. When an individual fails in the struggles to align the desire for social and economic well-being, acceptance, or satisfaction with cultural values, there is no personal dignity, rationales of whatever kind, notwithstanding.

Kurt could not let himself be accepted. He was a man completely nonaligned with the values of the people of this region. He walked the land as an individual, simply blind to what was going on around him. He said that he had been a good solider; that seemed to be enough. "I gud vit gun, en-so?" he would rhetorically ask. With a .22, he could shoot the eyes out of a squirrel at twenty yards. I am sure that Mark and I became excellent marksmen because of Kurt.

In my mind, however, Kurt was only half a man, more illusionary than real. Not that I have anything against illusions, for often we find more grace and simplicity there than in reality. He could not control his will or his body and was ruled by habit. He also treated Mark and me like we were his masters. He saw himself as a victim and victims can never be right in the head because they believe that something or someone "out there" has all power over them.

Happy breaks my thoughts about prisoners of war living in Wisconsin.

"Get Mark out here, and the both of you pick up the empty beer bottles. I'll get the drag and try to turn Kurt's mess into a field." While shouting out orders, Happy's normally white face had turned very red and very unhappy.

I pushed in the clutch and the tractor rolled to a stop. Putting the gearshift in neutral and setting the hand brake, I jumped off the seat and ran to get Mark.

I didn't say anything to Happy because I didn't know what to call him: Happy, Will, Dad? Mostly I got by simply by not calling him anything. I could have, should have, just asked him; "What do you want me to call you?" But I didn't. Besides, I thought, Happy would or could not answer the question anyway. Graceless and innocent, both of us wanted to love each other, but we didn't know how.

Every day of that first spring was filled with tractors, cows, machinery, and horses, planting, and cleaning the house. Mark and I were always discovering something new. The country world was full of secrets, and there was joy in just seeing all this new world had to offer. It also offered a lot of work, and it was hard work.

By the end of our first month, Mark and I were in the habit of rolling out of bed at 5:15 and starting the milking by 5:30. Mark would start cleaning the barn, while I helped Happy with the milking. By 6:30, Mark headed for the house to help with breakfast. By 6:45, Happy and I made sure that all the milk was cooling in the milk house and let the cows out for their exercise. We would then walk to the house for breakfast.

At about 8:00, we were back in the barn putting silage and grain in the mangers, letting the cows back in the barn, providing them with enough hay for the rest of the day, and then we started the day's real work. We discussed and planned about preparing the fields for planting, fixing fences, painting the inside of the milk house, and on and on. In the late afternoons, from about 5:30 to 7:30, we would do the afternoon milking, which always seemed to me to be a little more "leisurely" than the morning chores.

It was the same pattern every day until mid-April, when the cows could stay out in the pasture all day and night and come to the barn only to be milked.

While Happy and Mama would go to town every Saturday night to shop and have a drink at the Dew-Drop Inn, Mark and I pretty much entertained ourselves playing catch, listening to the radio, reading comics, and exploring the nearby woods and river. Whenever we could, we fished for trout in the many little streams that ran near and through the farm.

At first, we just used a cane-pole and worms. Later, as we came to appreciate the intelligence of trout, we learned to use fly rods. Over the years, both Mark and I became capable of casting a fly into the narrowest of streams. The drops falling from that invisible line into the moving stream will forever remind me of the craft involved and beauty of any harvest, including the harvest of trout. There was always the trade-off. In this case, two or three nice trout in my wicker pouch, and a hundred wood ticks on my pants, hands and arms.

As April moved toward May, Mama asked us and Happy about going to church. This seemed strange in our new place.

Though both Mama and Happy were Catholic, they didn't go to church. At first, Mark and I thought she forgot. In Chicago, Mama insisted that we go to church. She didn't care which church; she just said, "Go." So every Sunday Mark and I would sample houses of worship, rating their excitement or boredom levels.

One week, we went to the Greek Orthodox Church, the next week to the Armenian, then the Lutheran, the Baptists, and on and on, until we had covered every church within a five-mile radius north and west of Chicago's Loop. It got to be a habit, without being an addiction.

On the farm, we had not been to church in over three months and didn't miss it. Some habits leave you in a heartbeat. I remember once, when I was about nine, asking Mama why she didn't go to church, and suggested that I was worried about her soul.

"Church isn't about your soul. Your soul is between you and God. Church is about your community." Mark and I would eventually attend church, but that would be for different reasons, and the reasons had to do with neighborhood kids.

Even though we had been here since March, it wasn't until a beautiful early May afternoon that we met some of the "neighborhood" kids. About a quarter mile from our house stood a one-room schoolhouse. The school was on the main road, at the end of one of our fields, and sat in front of a little hill. On the other side of the hill stood a small woodlot and another field beyond. The receding hill and field led to some swampland that turned into a small lake in the spring. The little school building wasn't red, but a light blue, with white window frames, and a wood-shingled roof.

We watched kids going to school every day and just thought ourselves lucky to have the opportunity to skip it all. Sometimes we thought that the school would discover that we lived at this house and would come and take us to school. We were familiar with truant officers in Chicago, and this thought was both exciting and frightening at the same time.

By the middle of May, the school year ended and the teacher and students seemed to be enjoying a school picnic—a celebration of spring. They must have seen us outside, and a girl of about Mark's age came across the field to invite us to the celebration.

Mark and I also looked on with some envy at the ball field and swings behind the school and with some curiosity at the outdoor toilets and woodshed. According to Mama's plan, Mark would be going there in the fall. I would be going to New Kassel on the school bus to Jefferson High School. But now, we were both eager and a little anxious to meet people our own age, and maybe, just maybe, play some baseball!

9

WE WALKED SOFTLY ONTO THE PLAYGROUND. I was feeling some joy in being asked to the picnic, yet apprehensive about being the new guy. Newness has its advantages, but for this thirteen-year-old, uncontrollable self-consciousness began to build inside and interfere with joy. Several girls smiled at us, and they looked at us in an unusual way. We looked too. Mark and I hadn't seen a girl, our age, up close, in almost three months. Smiling, one of them sort of skipped up to us. "Hi. I'm Allison. That's Amy, Karen, Mary, Jane, and the quiet one over there is Elizabeth."

"What's your name?"

"Mike, and this is Mark."

"Come with me, we'll get some sandwiches in the schoolhouse." Without thought, Mark and I followed her into the old building and she led us to a large table filled with sandwiches, salads, and something called hot dishes, which were novel to us, but had new and wonderful flavors.

"Fill up a plate and come outside." Allison ordered. "Oh, if you want water, you can get it from the bubbler." I learned, among other things, that in Wisconsin, a bubbler was a ceramic water drinking fountain. That day, I would also learn some other things that would confuse and excite me for some time.

The girls expressed a friendliness and tacit sexuality that I had never noticed before. Maybe it was thirteen-year-old thinking. Maybe it had something to do with living right out in the open—on the farm, in the elements. I had learned a great deal about the land and farming in a few months, but they just seemed to know so much more.

There was a different sort of openness here. These girls were different; they seemed to confront life—maybe all of life, including death. These girls had to deal with all kinds of in-your-face challenges. The kids here carried wood to heat the school. They helped clean the school and shoveled snow off the sidewalk from the school door to the road and mailbox. They dressed the little first graders and took them to the toilet or out to play. At home, they knew about and dealt with animals. There were no modern spins on the topics of life to obscure the conversation. Perhaps this is what made them so open and relaxed about their own adolescent bodies, even in front of new boys.

I wasn't relaxed, and it sure didn't look as though the boys who were playing ball behind the school were any too relaxed either. Was this just the way it was? Are country girls different? Were they flirtatious or just being natural? Maybe I was just seeing girls for the first time.

There were many things and feelings that I was experiencing for the first time. Perhaps the opportunity for better personal relationships was one of them. Anyway, through the friendships that began to develop on that little schoolyard, I would discover an internal timidity that seemed far out of line with a teenage psyche. Later, I would learn a better definition of me as a teenager—unreflective and aggressively timid.

It's funny how shyness can often bring out the jerk in you. And "jerk-ness" always presents itself in shades of misconduct. The lesson I would need to learn is that misconduct can lead to violence, even self-inflicted violence, all are the results of incompetence. Perhaps, social incompetence is the most devastating dis-ease confronting all of us, as individuals and as societies. If we insist on being incompetent, we will be or become violent. From slapping your friend, to cheating in a ball game, or on your taxes, to waging war, to ... all are manifestations of incompetence—the end result of ignorance and child neglect.

In our culture, we wrongly avoid humility and place much worth on assertive behavior. So the shy ones among us, rather than exposing any sign of that ineptitude, will hide this lack of skill or social stigma.

The disruptive child in fifth grade, for example, is disruptive because he feels incompetent—never took the time to read the assignment or didn't finish his homework. This is a condition of character, not curriculum. To hide his shame, he will disrupt the class in an effort to veil his lack of character and knowledge.

Even the very bright "social incompetents," from parent to President, will work to change social context rather than change themselves. Part of it is a lack of social energy, no doubt, but to some degree, energy is also about competence. Some people believe that changing their context or location without changing their skills and character is better or, at least, easier. Besides, if we hide well enough, we won't have to change, even if a more meaningful life, better love relationships, and one's life work are the costs.

Character is built not on what happens to you, but how gracefully you respond to whatever is thrown your way. Character is formed not so much on battlefields or fields of play, but through engagement with and loyalty to other humans. Without this consideration and courtesy to others, little loyalty can be given to friend, family, or country. By giving priority to a higher or natural law, character demands thoughts and behaviors that simply provide the context to be better, happier, and capable of leaving a positive impact on those who follow.

Mark and I sat on swings to eat our picnic lunches, trying our best not to have to talk too much. The day was beautiful and the air humid, yet sweet with the smells of late spring, food, the slight hint of young girls' perfume, and the dirt of the ball field.

"Are you Italian, or something?" Amy asked.

"Armenian." Mark blurted out.

"What's that?" she continued.

"It's an old culture, the first Christian nation in the world," I contributed, seemingly defensive, allowing some of my uncle's influence to slip by my lips.

"Are you Christian?" Mark asked, trying, not too hard, to hide his sarcasm.

"Lutheran," Karen states with some pride. "We're all Lutherans, except for Liz—she's Catholic. That's why she's so shy."

"Happy—your new dad—he's Catholic, too. They go to the same church," Amy adds.

"I know that! It's the only Catholic church around," Karen shoots back.

"Or is it the Dew-Drop Inn he attends every Sunday?" Amy adds with sweet disapproval.

I was taken aback. Amy, the beautiful girl with such blue and quiet eyes, just put us down with such ease. I felt reduced. This would not be the last time we would be singled out as "different" or "less than."

Perhaps some people feel that insults or tearing someone else down validates their identity. Local knowledge, or inappropriate inferences, always make the jerk look wise or like a wise-ass. Being an "outsider" is hurtful when the jokes are covert, yet pointed right at you.

It was clear that Amy knew more about Happy than I did, and she was capable of using that knowledge. What was behind her calm eyes? And I wondered what she saw behind mine.

Mark wasn't as reflective and didn't seem able to hold back a slur of his own.

"Remember, Mike," he said for all to hear. "The Lutheran church seemed the most boring of all the churches we went to in Chicago."

"But the music and singing were nice," I added, trying to counter Mark's comment. Sometimes I wish that I could let the debate, argument, or fight just happen, but I'm such an avoider of conflict; I go out of my way to calm the waters. Even though this behavior never really feels good. Yet, right now, I did feel the desire to "go to church," perhaps to be like the rest of these people. I wanted to belong. Belonging seems right—right now.

What is ironic about this little discussion among the swings is that in the end, both Mark and I would become Lutherans, and within a year, I would be confirmed. The people here would have their influence.

Our lunch was interrupted with, "Want to play a little baseball?"

"Of course," I said under my breath.

"Of course," I shouted.

I wolfed down the sandwich, pushed Mark, and crossed the yard to the diamond in quick time. They were playing softball, but with gloves. That looked strange to me. I notice that the ball was smaller than the ones we used in Chicago. Baseball was baseball, but maybe softball was regional.

Back home, in Chicago, we used a fourteen-inch "clincher" with stitching inside the ball and played without gloves. These guys were playing with an eleven-inch stitched ball, like a baseball is stitched, and everyone had a glove, even the pitcher. There were only enough guys for five on each team. The girls didn't play, but they watched, like it was their job. Mark and I would bring the number to six on a side.

The other boys insisted that we play on the same team, so two boys went over to the opposing team. Mark and I threw the ball back and forth a few times and went out to play in the field without gloves. I didn't mind. In fact, I was so happy to be playing ball that I would have played without shoes. I positioned myself at shortstop or left side of the infield while Mark ran to the outfield.

They were all watching the new kids, I thought, and we're playing on this very rough infield. "No errors, don't screw up," I say to myself, and kept thinking, "Play the ball, don't let it play you. Pick up any grounder on the short hop or big hop, anything in between will handcuff you. It's the golden rule of playing the field." I repeated it over and over again, as I took a closer look at the sand and gravel.

Rough. The ground was very rough, and the whole field small. It made everyone seem bigger. The first and third base lines did not make a 90-degree angle at home plate. It was more like 70 degrees. The road forced the first base line in, while the hay field did the same to third. The outfield was uphill and ended about 110 feet from home plate in an open field soon to be planted in corn.

These were Happy's fields, and the county owned the road that went to Lee's house, one of our neighbors. These borders marked the ball field, and that was that. Our team had a first baseman, Oscar; a pitcher, Ivan; me on the left side of the infield, Mark in right field. Keith, a very large kid who would become a good friend, played in left field, and we had a catcher, Tommy. The other team was made up of all eighth graders. They all seemed a little bigger in size than our team, except for me and Keith, who, as an eighth grader, was already over six feet. Tommy and Ivan were in fifth grade and Oscar in sixth. Mark was going into seventh grade.

Ivan's first pitch was hit on the nose so hard and so right at me that I had no choice but to catch it in my bare hands, to the surprise of all who are watching and to my surprise as well.

"One out," I shouted. I really wanted to yell, "Damn, that stings."

Their second hitter was Lee, a big kid with too much anger on his face. On Ivan's second pitch, Lee hit a high fly to left field, right to Keith, who dropped it. By the time Keith found the ball,

Mark was on it. Lee had already reached third and was headed for home. Tommy was nowhere to be found, so I ran to cover home as Mark threw a strike to the plate. The ball got there a split second before Lee and I put the tag on him.

The next thing we all heard was Karen, "You're out, Lee!" Lee turned and looked at me with anger, but said nothing. Karen, on the other hand, felt no need for silence and shouts, "He's taking your girlfriends away."

Shit, I thought. Can't we just play ball here?

Ivan, who impressed me as a very good athlete, struck out the next hitter, Rob. Now we were up. The bottom of the first, no outs, no score, and Ivan led off with a hit to center. After Mark fouled off two pitches, both of which would have been hits if the foul lines had been correct, he beat out a grounder. In high school, Mark became a solid long-ball hitter. Built like a little bull, he would, in a few years, lead his high school in home runs and to a conference championship.

Two on, and it was my turn at bat. It just felt so good to be at the plate. I swung the bat a few times making sure that the second knuckles on both of my hands were aligned. I learned the knuckle-alignment trick by accident hitting clinchers in Chicago. I could always get an extra thirty feet or so just by using this simple placement of my hands. I guess it would make your wrists break through the ball at a higher speed adding significantly more power to the swing.

Lee's first two pitches were balls, one high, the other way inside. But the third pitch was right down the middle, just sitting there, waiting to go for a ride. I obliged and sent it over the center field fence and several yards into the plowed field.

This would be a short game, only three innings, and it ended as quickly as it started. No one kept score, and most of the kids just said they had to go home to do chores. Sure enough, a few parents came by in cars or pick-up trucks and in a few minutes, alone, Mark and I started to walk home.

The afternoon was good. The baseball, the girls, the food, even the slight chance of meeting new athletes and for them to know a little something about us. It was all good. I thought that we should be friends since some of us would play high school sports together, and this could be home.

I was still having trouble with the idea of "home." I knew about our home in Chicago; my father and uncle, our alcoholic stepdad, and a mother about to leave. On the other hand, I felt that the kids we met this afternoon created stories about my life based on the few facts that they had, and then read those stories as images of something not entirely true. No doubt, I looked, talked, and played differently. But they had only a few facts, and from those facts, they were trying to spin their own notions of truth.

It is important to understand that the stories of your past are created not only by you, but by others as well, and those stories will necessarily inform your present. People create contexts, or boxes, for their families and friends. So you need to be careful about having others create your life's stories, as we all end up carrying those stories of identity into the future, be they negative, neutral, or positive.

We understand so little about the nature of knowing that we are pushovers to the vanities of family stories. But they have a purpose tied to the nature of how meaning is created. The general purpose of personal stories, as well as history, is to give meaning and safe passage to our sacred images into a problematic future. To a large extent, our behavior is based on our image of the future. That future, like our past, is created from subjective knowledge that transcends the fragility of nature and science, and embraces a consciousness that we think is everlasting. However, there is but one way to focus ourselves in the world and that is to gain mutual understanding through real conversations. That is, we would listen to and consider the ideas and perspectives of different people, from different places and times, and explore the question: What does it take to live a loving and lovely life?

As the weeks and years have passed, old friends and new friends would eventually share pictures and tell stories about our lives. Those stories were interesting only to the degree that we became united in a common conversation. That was, and still is, the case because the comfort of common culture is possible only when the stories are constructed and shared together. To this day, old friends can still remember together. We all know what the other is thinking, and laugh, remembering together—not because it was true, but because we constructed it together.

More common, however, is that people living at the same time and in the same place will often construct different truths because they have created different stories. This happens in families, in churches, in businesses, and on baseball teams. We also and easily make outsiders of people to the degree that we do not allow them to create, with us common stories that evolve through the sharing of life's time, earth's locations, and significant adventures.

Just because you tell a person your story a hundred times, without conversation, he or she will never become part of your story. Those people who are systematically denied access to creating common stories run the risk of becoming our families' and nation's ogres. What's more interesting is that even when people through middle or older age live common lives together, they create stories that do not possess the same power of the stories they created as children or young adults. And as we age, these childlike tales are the narratives that seem to define the roles we play. Like more nascent tribes, we hold on to the deeds, taboos, and fairy tales even when boring the hell out of non-tribe members with stories devoid of mutual conversations.

Meaning may be tied to reason, but is more responsive to emotion, fantasy, and common bonds. At thirteen, I had no pictures, no bonds. Maybe it was time to get a camera. It certainly was time to engage in conversations and make and share experiences because without them, life's story quickly turns lonely and meaningless.

10

By the end of May, all the crops, including the corn, were planted and growing. The cows were in their summer pasture, and attention now turned to the first crop of hay to be cut and harvested in early to mid-June. The second crop, off the same field, would wait for August and the vagaries of the weather.

Of all the jobs on the farm, I grew to like haying the best. Cutting and raking hay were sensory adventures done alone without any sense of loneliness. You could let your imagination play as your mind watched the work, complete with its beauty and danger. Haying had its special smells—cutting, raking, baling, and stacking in the barn's mow—all unbelievably pleasant, and each with its unique perfume. I liked to think that the hay captured the sun so the cows could warm themselves in winter. As the sun warmed the hillside and pushed away the dew, the urge to hug the land sometimes overwhelmed me.

There are people in our lives not unlike the sun—understanding them must be indirect, or they'll burn you. The irony is that while you would like to be in love without the burn, it is not possible. The secret is in the balance and in knowing that joy will also extort pain. Love and pain come as a set, and we must accept both.

In the years since, Mark and I have discussed the values we hold—values like fairness, the importance of work, and learning.

We have tried to consider where those values and our behavior controlling myths came from. Given the circumstances of our early lives, we wonder still today, how we survived, and to some degree even prospered. We never had the luxury of being kids. We played ball and went to school, but also had the life-challenging responsibilities of finding something to eat, doing chores, and, at the same time, building reputations. We had been on our own since we were eight and six years old. The cost to the two of us was great. We really never got to know each other. We had little idea of who the other was. And, we believed strange things, both good and evil, about each other—beliefs devoid of any realty. Growing older never seems to change the dynamic, perhaps because myth and emotions overtake the intellectual power of reality.

11

IN UNCLE'S EPIC STORY, THE KNIGHT CHLOVLY spoke and acted out the synthesis of love (truth) and pain (knowledge), blurring the boundaries between enchantment and our everyday sensibilities. Uncle told these stories during walks, putting us to bed, and even at dinner. He would create a whole different world for us to enter.

Uncle would tell the story and then ask questions. In one of Chlovly's most famous battles, the knight engaged the Devil and his army of the underworld. The battle raged for three days and three nights. On the third day, Chlovly, always in the thick of the battle and continually fighting without sleep, cut his own arm and rubbed salt into the wound believing that the pain would help him stay awake.

"He is magnificent in battle," said Uncle, "destroying the enemy almost as quickly as they appear while encouraging his army on."

At the end of the third day in what seems like the twilight of earth, the Devil, in his own cunning way, tries to recruit Chlovly to command his underworld horde, the highest in rank next to Lucifer.

"Why me?" Chlovly asked.

"Because more impressive than your power as a warrior is your character and your love of God," said the Devil. "As long as love has even a hint of living on, I will never achieve complete domination of people's minds. I've come close to destroying love, but one of His own always gets in the way, and you are in my way. "

And now the Devil makes his offer.

"You have free will and can decide to be with me or not. If you come with me, I will grant you power, glory, and wealth, the likes of which the world has never seen. You will be my son. We will burn the souls of all men."

Unlike Chlovly, I felt that I didn't have free will. When you're a boy, it's easy to be confused and believe that the world belongs to the Devil and you are unarmed to withstand it, and hardly able to challenge and succeed at anything. I feared Chlovly's character. It demanded too much. My instinct was to run and hide. My problem was not just poverty, but innocence— a deep ignorance of the world. Chlovly knew how to engage the Devil. He knew how to stand up against unpleasantness. He simply embraced his power of love because he knew who he was and what was at stake.

Leaning closer to Chlovly and in a whisper, the Devil continues, "I was with God at the beginning, and thought myself wise enough to understand God's purpose. But God's purpose is in His performance, and His performance is rhetorical, a vapor, designed to affect our minds into believing that his Word is immutable and authoritative. I left God's presence, not all together voluntarily, because I could see no window on Truth."

Chlovly thought for a moment; "But I understand the ritual to be good and true. Beauty is in the act, the dance, the love, the performance. Truth is not some lost jewel you find after years of searching; it is the quality of your quest. Your performance produces Truth, and gives meaning by linking that performance with thought and feelings. Our performances are not experienced as metaphors. They are immediate, transparent, and unconstrained. And, they are always new."

Chlovly continues, now nose to nose with the Devil, "The great irony is that it's not love but fear that makes us think that we are God-like, and your fearful metaphors become the controlling myths of our lives. Your problem, Sir, is that you want to find the jewel without paying attention to performance. You want treasure without the work.

As a child, Uncle's stories were about adventure. I understood the words, buy not the meaning in the story. As a man, I now see that the stories were about the contradictions of life that can't be reconciled with logic, suggesting a deeper mystery beyond the sequences we ascribe to life, from birth to death. The stories were never really about God or the Devil; they were about the power of the human mind.

Chlovly concludes, "Our moral imagination is defined through the stories we tell. Like it or not, Devil, you are part of those stories, and an actor in the larger human drama. You teach us that we are in an internal struggle between good and evil, and that this struggle goes on within the same person, same family, and same society. Truth is in the struggle, in the argument, in the tensions of our many performances. And the truth is always contested. Without the struggle, we are just natural. But because of you, we have the opportunity to be armed and engage such virtues as courage, truthfulness, charity, compassion, and industry, in service to defeat selfishness, ignorance, pride, and laziness. There is no magic here except in the struggle that moves our heart and self toward acts of love. Your offer of unearned wealth and notoriety carries with it pride, jealousy, and greed—meaningless all. No thank you! It is time to return to the struggle and continue our battle."

12

Even as I began—and still try—to understand the people and land around the farm, Chlovly's words seemed to be the common knowledge of every farmer who engages each new dawn. Holding the ideas of love and fear in your head at the same time is not a common skill. Yet, the farmer knows that love and fear, sun and burn, life and death, help define each other. The farmer thinks about these contradictions as nature's balance.

They likely wouldn't say it, but farmers understand the balance in their lives are found in knowledge and practice of farming, and the criticism of such. The knowledge and wisdom necessary for land care are found in fundamental themes. Knowledge, with criticism, can illuminate purpose. They are parts of the same whole. Each of these ideas defines itself in terms of the others. For example, love is defined in beauty and truth. Just as beauty is defined in love and truth, and truth in beauty and love.

To preserve life, we must love it. I think Happy loved the land, his cows, beer, but I wondered about loving his own life. Not just wanting to live it—but loving it. I wondered about my life too—still do.

The question that farmers would tacitly ask was about the "best" ways to do this or that. They would put rules aside in favor of looking for an innate harmony. People who seemed to live their lives well tend to base their decisions on an innate, subjective truth found in balance, aesthetics, and symmetry. Keep your eyes and mind open and test your generalizations. That practice will reveal virtue—and virtue will define good rules.

To a farmer, doing the right thing or being virtuous is nothing less than having perspective. The farmer creates harmony by actively working with the soil, weather, animals, machinery, and human relationships, perhaps in that order. Harmony is virtue. Virtue is seeing far. Virtue, in this regard, is a balancing act. I can love the hayfield in harmony with the weather, soil, and so forth. And, as we look for better, more aesthetic methods and models, criticism becomes a natural attribute of this love.

Meaning comes from listening to the land and hearing the subtle songs of the landscape. When taken together, I can say I love, improve, and find meaning in this work, at this time, in this place. And that is enough.

Here on this farm, the performances of our lives and their meaning began to give a new ring to the power of Uncle's stories. Chlovly was right; dying—even spiritual death—is easy. It is the struggle to create love and meaning that is hard.

13

THE CADENCE OF SUMMER ON A DAIRY farm creates a dance with nature that is precariously beautiful. The days are filled with work and good exhaustion; the nights are filled with easy and deep sleep. The milking chores that dominated my spring, in summer receded into incidental chores that were overwhelmed by the demands of caring for and harvesting the crops, the vegetables in the garden, and the fruit from the apple trees.

We also picked raspberries in the pastures and woods beyond. Mama canned the berries. Not too many weeks after, we picked apples which we wrapped one-by-one in newspaper and placed them in wooden barrels in the unheated root cellar in the basement. They would stay good and firm until after Christmas.

Happy, Mark, and I, and sometimes Kurt, would bring in the hay, cultivate the corn, and by late August, start harvesting and threshing the oats. After the first frost, we'd start cutting corn for the silo. We would also spend several cool, clear September days picking ears of corn and later, around Halloween, husking them for storage in the corn cribs. Those ears would be ground up with oats and an assortment of minerals to create a grain mix that the cows would eat all winter.

In between these activities, Mark and I attended church—the Lutheran church—mostly out of curiosity and a chance to see some of those kids we played ball with in May. I also met and liked the pastor, Jim Shaneburger, who convinced us to join Luther League. This set us upon the road to confirmation. Luther League took us to events where we met new kids from all over the state. I enjoyed these times as a complement to the chores back home.

One beautiful Wednesday evening, I rode along with our neighbor Butch to a softball game under the lights. Now a farmer in his late forties, Butch, in his younger days, was a good baseball player. Along with other older local athletes, they would work their farms during the day and twice a week play softball under the lights, trying to recapture the glories of the past. It was all very serious, and almost every local tavern in the region sponsored a team, which amounted to more than enough teams for an eight-team league.

Baseball happened on Sunday afternoons, and was for the few. These teams were sponsored by town and city businesses, as well as individuals in a four-county region. City pride was evident in these home-talent leagues. The lineups included college athletes, home for the summer, a few older guys in their thirties and forties, some of whom had made a try to play professional ball, a few high school kids, and even one or two older players who had once been outstanding ballplayers. The home-talent leagues let them swing a bat and throw a ball for just a bit longer.

The softball leagues provided a way for some guys to stay in shape for the Sunday games that almost all of the townspeople and farmers attended. While traveling to the games, fans listened to the Chicago Cubs and later the Milwaukee Braves and then watched their boys play the foreigners from twenty miles away. The radio and the local baseball games made me feel like I was at home. I didn't know it then, but by next summer, I would be playing second base and at times shortstop on our home-talent team every Sunday. On Friday nights, and some Saturdays I'd play for the American Legion team located in another town some thirty miles from home.

Happy was fine with taking me to the Legion games when I couldn't find another ride. Our home-talent team had a bus for away games, so all I had to do on Sunday was get from church to the bus. On those Sundays when we played home games, Mark and I would catch a ride home with our neighbor, get a little lunch, and ride back to town again with any one of a number of people who were going to the game. The home-talent league had teams in little towns and a few cities throughout the state of Wisconsin. The American Legion conference had teams only in the larger cities.

In less than a year, I got to know the abilities of baseball players in the area. Most of all, I started again to know and be with baseball, and better understand my strengths and limitations. These qualities mostly applied to my athletic abilities, not necessarily to my qualities as a human being. Happy soon became proud of me and even prouder of Mark, who, in five years, would be hitting homeruns on Sunday afternoons.

On one late Sunday afternoon in mid-August before Labor Day, we had a visit from Coach Anderson, who came to meet me as well as Mark. The news of two new athletic boys in town, one who would be enrolling in high school in a few weeks, finally made it to Coach's attention and he must have thought that it was time to meet the family.

Mr. Anderson was an insurance salesman in town who had played baseball and basketball at the local high school and at one of the state's Division III state colleges. They say he was a star and could have played pro in either sport. Even though he was not a teacher, he coached the two sports at Jefferson High. Throughout the summer, I watched him in the home-talent league. He was good, but too heavy and slow, I thought. He was a natural, who, with the right attitude, perhaps, could have moved up.

Coach showed up at the farm just before chores on a damp and drizzling day. Mama had an early supper prepared before milking and asked Mr. Anderson to join us.

"Can't stay, I need to get home soon. My wife is expecting me for dinner. Just wanted to meet the boys." He stumbled over his words and it appeared that he had been drinking some that afternoon. Mama was incensed. He never even looked at her. She was probably thinking that most everyone drinks around here.

"Let's walk up to the barn," Coach said, without properly acknowledging Mama or her meal—a big mistake. Nevertheless, we walk to the barn to see if we could install a basketball goal in the hayloft.

"You need to work hard if you expect to play for me. You understand work?" I wanted to tell him to stop and leave before he insulted us anymore. Insults come in easy and subtle ways. Mark and I didn't seem like the other kids around here. Too dark, too different, something, I don't know. Discrimination was something that we would learn about in greater detail. Discrimination was something Mama already knew too much about.

With complete insensitivity, Coach started to tell Mama about the benefits of playing ball. "Athletics will teach your boys leadership, sportsmanship, and sacrifice…" and Mama just listened. I wished for his own health that he would not say any more and just leave.

What Coach didn't know about Mama was that she had little time for pronouncements. She was much more concerned about respect, and like Chlovly, she was more into performance, and performances had beginnings, middles, and end points. When the act was over, it was over. No need to celebrate, no need to cry; the beauty or despair was in the doing.

My hunch was that she was given little respect throughout her life. For the most part, she was alone. Few, if any, understood her mind and the despondency of being an uneducated, middle-aged woman in a segregated, masculine, and increasingly technological world. She hoped to be worldly, but knew she was just an "ethnic" on the fringes of US society. She wanted to be part of the bigger society but was locked by time and circumstance into a more tribal and closed existence. There were places she couldn't go, things she couldn't do.

The cultural claustrophobia must have been almost unbearable for her. She was far too smart to be in such a dilemma. Engaging Mama was like walking on a mine field. I never knew if I should, or if I even could, embrace or reject her, and that ambivalence haunts me still.

"I don't know about basketball so I stay out of the way," she says to Mr. Anderson.

I think I should be quiet. I want her to disengage right now. My wish is granted as she walks back to the house.

We reach the hayloft. The rain is falling gently but with increasing intensity. Mark, Happy, Coach, and I look silently at the barn floor. The new hay is now all in the lofts, leaving just the center mow with any room for the basket and backboard. The oak-plank floor has been worn smooth and silky from the many years and loads of hay that have crossed it.

We study the dimensions for a few moments, saying nothing.

"Here," Coach says, "let's put the basket here."

"You need to build a backboard, but I have a basket and net in the car, and two old basketballs for you two to use. They're on me. Wait here and I'll get them." He returns promptly, dampened by the rain, with basket and balls in an old feed bag. He removes one ball and throws it at me. "Let me see you pass it back," he shouts.

I throw it back with one hand as he did. "Let me show you how to pass the ball." Coach moves within ten feet of me and says, "This is a chest pass. Snap your wrists. This is a bounce pass. You use the same wrist motion—see—snap"

He shows us several other kinds of passes—one-hand baseball, hook, and two-hand overhead. "Practice, OK. Practice."

We thank him for the basket and balls and tell him that we will put up the basket and backboard tomorrow; maybe even after milking tonight. And we did. For countless days and nights to come, always after milking, Mark and I, together with others in our farm neighborhood spent time playing in the barn, right through the winter and into spring. Happy always knew where to find us; he would just listen for the pounding of dribbling on the oak barn floor.

"It's time to eat."

"There's Mama. We'd better go."

Approaching the back porch before Mark and Happy, she asks, "Is that other guy staying for supper?"

"No, he said he can't stay."

"Well, get washed up."

We had a meal of salad, roast chicken and potatoes, with pie to follow. For me, eating after milking is better than before. I hate the idea of going out to the barn after being cleaned up and relaxed for dinner. On Sunday, though, things were different. We often combined lunch and dinner and ate a larger meal about three or four o'clock.

Today was no different, except that John Anderson had come over and it was now almost five. Things had a chance of becoming tense because we were so late, and the cows always had to be milked close to the same time each day, so we were all quieter than usual as we sat around the table. My mind, however, was still back in the hayloft, and I was caught off guard by Mama's announcement.

"I am leaving for Chicago in two weeks. The new bathroom, the new tractor, and the other work we did around the house have left us with too many bills. I need to go back to work so the mortgage doesn't continue to grow faster than the two of you."

"But in Chicago?" I ask.

"But what will we do without you?"

"If you go, I go, too." Mark threatens.

"Don't worry; I'll be back once a month. From town, the train runs right to Chicago. Don't worry."

Things had been going well, I thought, and now she dropped this bomb. I know that Mark will go with her. He's that stubborn. Once he makes up his mind, he'll do it. I feel sorry for him, but, hell, I will be alone with Happy and sometimes Kurt. The gravity of that thought was so heavy that my stomach hurt to the point of nausea.

It's just a misunderstanding; she couldn't be serious. I thought that the deal of moving out here was that we would have a family, a home. It seems that things are always just taken away—my dad, our home, Chicago, school, and now Mark and Mama.

I left the table and ran to the barn and started getting the cows ready for milking. My eyes are filled with tears and my head feels so stuffed I can barely see what I'm doing.

All of these things, and more, did come to pass. Mama and Mark left within two weeks. She did return each month, but I would not see Mark until Christmas and he would not return for good until the next summer. I would hardly recognize him.

Her trips home became less frequent as time went by and Mama did not return to stay with us for almost four years. I was a senior then. She left again the following year and did not return until Mark was a senior.

I remember the many things Mark and I didn't have or couldn't take for granted. One was security. Another was food—just something good to eat. Often, our breakfast was a piece of toast and supper a can of soup or beans. Without a grocery store down the block, it took us—and particularly me—a long time to learn how to feed ourselves.

We did drink a lot of milk. It was right from the cows and free. After Mark's return, things looked up a little. He became a pretty good cook, and we developed a workable system to divide our labors around house chores. Mark was definitely the cook, and both Happy and I were thankful about that.

If stability is missing from his life, but a child doesn't know any better, does it matter? Does it impact identity? Can you really construct an identity by yourself? Are identity and meaning possible without real love and relationships? I felt like I was aboard a ship that was always sailing for a sunny isle, but somehow knew I would never be allowed to come ashore.

14

SOMETIME THAT LATE SUMMER, HAPPY and I were discussing my age and he suggested that the young should be happy, by definition, because they're young. But back then, I often felt sad perhaps of feeling disconnected. Certainly not always happy. I didn't even know what I desired, and I didn't know that to desire something is not necessarily desirable. I remember so many adults commenting on how their high school years were the happiest years of their lives and they wished they could go back and relive them, knowing what they know now, of course. I've always hoped that those people were wrong. I still believe they are. If they did know then what they know now, I wonder if happiness would be the result. Happiness is only a result, a byproduct, of good work and of being aware. It can be random, sometimes regrettable, but is not a goal.

We need to pay attention, particularly to our regrets, not to our resentments. We should try to reflect on them and give ourselves the chance of learning from them. Looking back sixty-some years, this is what I understand: the most painful regrets in life are the regrets of the young for doing, and the regrets of the old are for not doing. Happiness is not a list of things or activities, but about quality, harmony, and purpose. Happiness is in the pursuit, not in the having. It is in the doing, in the performance. But how do we know what to do, how to do it, and why? I don't know, but this knowledge seems to come through the tests life throws at us and our willingness to manage those trials with courage and grace. It's about reflecting honestly on history, and constantly changing the performance.

The performance must be done first for a principle, for someone or something outside ourselves. It's like a bank shot in basketball; it must bounce off of something or someone before it strikes home. The performance tests come with life choices that take us from the seemingly happy and easy to the painful and grievous.

As adults, we pay attention to our trials and absorb them, constructing our knowledge of how to prepare for change, and making it clearer with each new encounter. But I am not sure that even if we paid attention, we could evaluate our decisions in terms of happiness. All we can say, perhaps, is that with each new day we are blessed with another chance to live well. In the end, happiness is free will, judgment, and courage. At the end of life, happiness is something we judge alone.

In the end, happiness is the way we struggle to try to get beyond our base and unstable passions. In this effort, there is no difference between the Prince and the Pauper. Both will be happy only in the struggle and no disguise of finery will give advantage. In fact, all of us must be mindful in our judgments of others that we do not let the regalia of office interfere with our judgment of ourselves.

15

LABOR DAY ARRIVED COMPLETE WITH mixed feelings of anxiety and joy. Tomorrow, the yellow bus would arrive at our driveway and I would catch a ride to high school. My first day. A new school in a new life. Happy and I had gone shopping last week to purchase school clothes and now, the day before the start of the fall semester, I feel so alone. Mark and Mama are gone. They sent no letters and there is no way to call them. Alone, except for Happy.

After chores, we make supper. Roast beef and boiled potatoes and we talk a bit about tomorrow.

"This is the best time of your life," Happy proclaims. I could only think, "No way."

"Every period of life is the best and also the worst. You can do things now that you couldn't do last year and that you won't do years from now. What is special about youth is you are free from aches and pain and illness and you have so much energy. I wish I had that in front of me. I say high school years are the best times to have in front of you."

"Did you play ball in high school?"

"Didn't go."

"You didn't go to high school?"

"I only went up to the sixth grade, and that was as far as I could. Not uncommon in 1914. At my age, already twelve, I was a big kid, and the chores had to be done. I was lucky to make it that far. I wanted to play baseball just like you."

Just like you—the words came slowly and with sadness.

I could tell that Happy might have been a good athlete. Although overweight, he was quick, he was very strong, and he was agile. I liked the fact the he thought I could play ball and was positive about it.

"There will only be the two of us this winter and I just feel a little lost or alone," I said.

"Well, I do, too. And I have been alone forever. But let's be alone together."

And that was that.

I went to bed about 8:30, but sleep wouldn't come. At about midnight, I stepped into a star-filled night and walked down a shadowy road. I was feeling anxious about tomorrow and life in general. Returning home after thirty minutes, I got into bed and tried to still a nervous mind.

The next morning was filled with eagerness and lingering anxiety; I was feeling insecure about being different from those I would meet today.

"Mike, the bus will be here. Better get out there"

Going out the door, I call back. "I will go out for freshmen football, but I really want to give basketball and baseball a good shot."

"Just have fun," he said. "See you at five."

The patterns established on that day after Labor Day would follow me most of the days through high school: milking, 365 days a year at 5:30 a.m., breakfast, bus to school, classes, lunch, classes, practice or game, bus home, evening milking, dinner, a little radio, bed, some reading, and sleep—deep sleep. With variations on a theme, that was it. What the sequence doesn't show are the people, the activities, and the passions. What the sequence doesn't show are the aesthetic patterns necessary to live life well each day.

Walking down the driveway, Happy is on my mind and I feel good about his support of me on this day.

The day is pleasantly warm as I wait for the bus. I have on my new twill pants and a sport shirt—the pants gray, the shirt pinkish. As the bus approached on our gravel road, it worked up a large cloud of dust and I thought my new clothes would be covered with dust. The driver stopped and motioned me on.

"Mornin', son."

"Good mornin'," I return, and look for a seat.

The bus is about half full and I decide to sit by myself in the second row on the left, on the aisle. With the exception of a few kids in the back, people are sitting alone. There are both high school and elementary kids on board, and like me, most seem anxious and silent.

At the next stop, Keith gets on. He and I recognize each other. I slide over and he sits with me. He looks bigger than I remember when I saw him just a month ago in early August.

"Going out for football?" he asks.

"Yep," I respond.

"Good, we should have a good group of freshmen," he claims. "What position you goin' out for?"

"Uhhh, half back, maybe."

"Are you white or black?"

"What?"

"Some of us were talkin' the other day and we wondered."

"I don't know what that means, black or white." I say.

"Are you a Negro, like Jackie Robinson, or white? You know, your color, white or black?"

"I don't know. My hair is black, my skin is what? Olive? Certainly, it's a little darker than yours. But my father's family came from the Caucasus Mountains, where the word Caucasian comes from. I guess I am white. But I never thought about it until we moved out of Chicago."

Keith goes on; "Well, I was hoping you were at least part black. That way we might have someone like Jackie Robinson on our side."

"Wow," I thought. I saw Jackie play. What a weird compliment, if, in fact, it was.

"Well, in that case, maybe I am." I said.

My first bus ride on my first day of school started with a casual conversation on race, and without any historical knowledge of me or of human interactions created by migration patterns. I would learn much later that almost everyone is part black, or part red, or part yellow, or part whatever. In only a few weeks, in my English class, a theory was presented that claimed that at the beginning of the 9th century, the Moors said that the Mediterranean Sea was a Moorish lake and the people of Spain, Italy, and Greece were blonde before they got there. The Spanish Armada was comprised of many Moors, and as the story goes, when the storms in the English Channel destroyed most of the fleet during the reign of Queen Elizabeth I, many of the surviving sailors went ashore in Wales and Ireland, bringing knowledge and intermarrying with native peoples.

The middle and eastern parts of Europe, and from the Low Counties to Russia and south to Turkey, all have had immigrants from Asia and Africa. Human diversity is as profound as the several snowflakes.

Ignorance of history, biology, and psychology seems to drive the behavior of people. Since that September day in 1953, riding on a school bus to the village of New Kassel and Jefferson High School, I have wondered just why our schools don't teach us about how race is first and foremost a cultural and not a biological construct. The extension of our ignorance regarding race is breathtaking. Ignorant people seem certain about almost everything, and that notion of certainty haunts me continually.

I had known a lot of black kids in Chicago—some were good ball players and some stank. What's up with Keith? Does he believe that darker skin makes for a better player? Was this my introduction to race or ignorance?

Because most of the comments about people come from adults, kids like me begin to second-guess themselves. Keith's words may have originated from a desire to win ballgames. But the larger world was far beyond his innocent mind, so he and others created another, smaller, world.

Closing your mind and your community is comfortable for insiders, but very uncomfortable to anyone on the outside who has different life experiences.

Some can live with large categories of the world already set-up and certain. It's easy. This is your place, so stay there. This is your God, do what He says, and don't look for other explanations. Don't ask questions. Don't think, rely on your emotions, and just repeat what the powerful tell you because what the powerful say is what you should know.

Separate categories, no matter who creates them, give easy, but almost always incorrect, views of the world--even notions of right and wrong. Anyone who creates a closed society, has to also create large conceptual ambiguities. While wanting to keep the power of the status quo, he or she also knows that any created forms of beauty, truth, justice, and even happiness are only approachable in the debatable tensions that exist in the closed system.

What is truth? Is it high energy? Is it intellectual? You will never know unless you also seek an answer within the qualities of beauty or justice. In the end, it's all about conversation and relationships. There may be no naïve people, just people without the ability to see relationships.

Disjunctive sets seem to work best in mathematics, not so much in the social or physical worlds. If you're into easy, as most of us are, you go with your gut, and without any hesitation or reflection. Inclusive sets, on the other hand, are more difficult to conceptualize, calling upon hues, shades, and subtleties ignored by those who want to be pure and sure. There are large differences between the open mind and the closed. The former is based on thought, criticism, questions, uncertainty, and self-control, while the latter is built on acceptance, obedience, certainty, and external controls.

Most of us take the easy way, the child's way. Years later, these thoughts would come back and eat at me. And what would hurt more would be the feeble way I addressed the ignorance of my closed mind with all the timidity of the child. I didn't have the courage to state my anti-certainty argument. All I needed to say to myself or to Keith was, "Are you sure?" "How do you know?" "Do you understand the feelings of other persons, and your impact of the words on them?"

16

My first impression of Jefferson High School was—it was clean! The hardwood floors gleamed and the whole place smelled of fresh cleaning compounds. It was the kind of fresh that makes a janitor proud.

The school was divided into three somewhat equal parts: the academic wing, the agricultural wing, and the athletic wing. The academic and athletic spaces were connected to each other, while the agricultural and industrial building was located about twenty yards from the main campus. There were also a few smaller buildings that served as storage sheds for the lawn and grounds equipment. There were over three hundred students in the school, about seventy percent bused in from the farms and smaller towns in the district.

All in our new clothes, freshmen met in the gym for orientation and class assignments. We had little choice of classes: Algebra, biology, English Literature, and state and U.S. government were all first-year requirements. Physical education was also required if you didn't play sports—which meant that all the girls and about two-thirds of the boys took gym. The girls had no organized sports in which to participate, just the Girls' Athletic Association, which seemed to me like just another physical education class.

There were two elective choices. The first choice was between typing and agriculture. I took the latter as a way to understand farm work a little better. The second was a foreign language. Latin was offered for those, who for some reason, thought they might go on to higher education. I signed up still thinking there would be a university in my future. Four years later, at graduation, only three of us in our class would go on to college.

As soon as registration was completed, all freshmen boys who planned to go out for any sport met with the coaching staff in one of the two English classrooms. Both coaches were there, and the classroom was standing room only.

Coach Anderson greeted us with, "It looks like we have a good group of big kids this year. Sign up for the sports that interest you and pick up your insurance forms so you can get a physical and dental exam today. Doctor Cooper knows that you will be coming to the clinic today and the dentist's office has also been told."

Later that afternoon, I would make my first trip ever to a dentist's office. Fourteen years old and I had never seen a dentist. "Looks good," the dentist said, as he took a long drag on his cigarette, marked my green Wisconsin Interscholastic Athletic Association card and said, "Your teeth are in good shape; no cavities. Just keep brushing and whatever else you're doing."

In high school, I began to feel the lack of care, of affection, and even of material things in my life; feelings and things that other students just took for granted even in this poor region. And Mark was two years behind me, in line to experience even more neglect, but at the time, these thoughts were not in my mind. I was too busy with my sense of loneliness and trying to fit in. It took a great deal of energy.

Coach continued, "We start football practice at 3:30 today for those who finish your physicals, and for the rest of you, have it done by tomorrow. Go to the clinic at 3:00 today and run back to practice. Freshmen, it would be good for you to just watch the varsity today. Remember that the after-school-practice bus will run you home at 5:00; be ready at 4:55... Any questions?"

We all went through our shortened morning classes, met our teachers, ate lunch—which would become one of my high school highlights—and continued with an abbreviated afternoon class schedule.

Our algebra class was taught by Miss Holmes, a new teacher all of twenty-one years old, I guessed. She was dressed in a long, navy-blue wool skirt, a white sweater, and low-heeled, grayish shoes. She had a beautiful smile, was a little on the heavy side, and I liked her immediately.

Biology was taught by Mr. Krowe. He had run the science department for years and I ended up taking four different courses from him. He was a small, slight man who wore a white lab coat. He smelled like the chemistry room, said very little, loved to do experiments with us, and his soft voice had great intensity. His head seemed too large for the rest of his body, and too many students could never see beyond the scientist's appearance into the love he had—not for us, but for his subject matter. I thought him a great teacher though not my favorite.

That spot was filled by our English teacher, Mr. Michael Kennedy, a handsome Irishman from Brooklyn. It was from Mr. Kennedy that I first learned about the Moors and their impact on Europe.

He was a wonderful mix of genes and had come to study at St. Norbert College in De Pere because he had seen the Green Bay Packers play in New York and thought that it would be interesting to see where they came from. Either that, or he was running to or from something. He did graduate from St. Norbert's College and became a teacher. Most of our teachers were either very young or over fifty, he was in between, perhaps in his late thirties or early forties. He was married to one of the most beautiful women that I had ever seen—the kind you can't take your eyes off of, but, of course, can stare at for no more than a second or two. Mr. Kennedy had been in the Navy, and was wounded, not in service, but on the streets of New York. I could relate to his stories of the big city, and we became not friends, but teacher and student in the best sense of that relationship. We talked about all kinds of things, from how I could be a better actor in the school plays to why the plays of Shakespeare could teach us so much about ourselves. He said that wisdom could be found in Shakespeare because he teaches that life's questions are unanswerable. We are not permitted to know our own lives because we can't get out of them, and so cannot achieve perspective. Mr. Kennedy told me that reality has no order, narrative does, particularly Shakespeare's stories that ask us if we know exactly who we are.

I loved the opportunity to talk about such things. And, I think Mr. Kennedy did, too. However, at times, I wanted to scream, "Why can't I see what the hell he's talking about?" Think. I tried to think and read some of Shakespeare's plays and sonnets, but was left with little insight. I tried to follow Mr. Kennedy's arguments but after we stopped talking, the ideas would vanish as though I had amnesia.

Mr. Kennedy enjoyed sports of all kinds, but talked little about them. I always looked to see if he was in the stands when I played. He and his beautiful wife attended many games until he left teaching the spring of my junior year to take a job with a school-book publishing company.

I thought that Mama and Happy could also attend games. Maybe they would come to parents' night. That would be important to me because they would be introduced and I would have a family connection. That hope was ill-placed. They would attend no school events, not even graduation. Mark was my only family, but it took me years to understand that. And in the end, I lost him, too. I lost him through neglect. That is, I didn't understand that even family members must work on being close and concerned with and about one another. I didn't do the necessary work.

A new school offers a great opportunity to reconstruct one's narrative. A new school or a new location, or even a new friend, can open a new chapter in a life's story. Writing a new story is no trivial matter. To narrate a life, or even parts of it, is to open up a future both anticipated and unexpected. My life is not Mama's life, nor anyone else's. Others may help in writing my story, but it is my skill and my desires and character that will ultimately bring meaning to my life.

Beware of people who think they have their own true answers, I thought, as they are not only boring, they are dangerous. They diminish others and themselves because their minds cannot handle the complexities of life. They want everything in its place, role by role. This is what a mother is. This is a father. This is a son. This is a priest. They refuse to embrace the notion that truth is always contested. Without the conversations that bring together opposing ideas we cannot engage the more comprehensive pictures of life. Thus, they always look for approval of their idea, their truth. Of course, even when given approval, they won't believe it because their notion of truth is fixed within such small tolerances of reality and to see beyond would destroy their own lives. This is not the narrative I wanted to write for myself.

What seems altogether true is that the condition of certainty and the condition of uncertainty are both inadequate to the demands of living well. The secret may not be just in the quality of what we do, but also in the reasons we have for doing those things in the first place. We are rational and emotional beings at the same time.

There's an old story that tells why the craftsman and the dreamer are both important to quality, as well as to that rationale which links transcendent meaning to our behavior.

One day, a man came upon two people who were laying bricks along a city street.

He asked, "What are you doing?"

One bricklayer said, "I'm placing one brick upon another."
And, the other bricklayer said, "I'm building a cathedral."

Cathedrals cannot be built without design, art, and purpose; nor can a life.

17

Day two. On the second day, I was up at 4 a.m. and had most of the milking done before Happy came to the barn.

"What's gotten into you?" he asked.

"Nothing," was my only reply, never looking up from my place between two very large cows.

I didn't know how to think about my place in school, on this farm, in this family. All at once, my eyes were being opened and I didn't know what to look at first. I would have given anything for some advice here, some counseling, some support. But I had lots of work to do, and the opportunity to go to high school, to play ball, to talk to girls, and maybe even to learn something. I think I understood that high school was about those things, but the real learning was about self. Who would I be here in this new place?

I had no idea of the wide array of experiences that were available and no one to clue me in. Living without engaged parents, or any caring adult, means a lack of emotional nourishment, and it's equally harmful because there is no one around to open your mind to the opportunities found in living each day to the limit; helping you make better decisions about your character; and understanding how time should be used.

Without this assistance and support, I ran the risk of being ruled by instinct and letting time use me. Ironically, I have learned over the years that children with overprotective parents and children with parents who just don't care end up in the same place—lacking qualities of mind, body, and spirit, and becoming incomplete.

Children who have no guidance cannot open anything but random doors that may or may not lead anywhere. But the challenge is just as great for children who have all doors opened for them. Children need the gift of time and care so doors to the future can be carefully examined.

Adults often refuse to understand this. They want their kids to become adults and fast, without the necessary process of timely growth. Child rearing, like all other important things in life, if it's worth doing, it's worth doing slowly.

I need to get to the house, so I turn to Happy. "I'll start breakfast if you'll finish up here. I have to catch the bus in 35 minutes." I say, not wanting to talk.

"Sounds like you're feeling sorry for yourself. Don't! Things can always be worse," he says as I leave the barn.

Yep, at least I get to go to school while he needs to stay in the barn; that's worse. As we age, each of us constructs our own psychological barn from which we see the world. The trick is not to believe that our perception is all there is to reality. At least I have this limited advice; "Don't feel sorry for yourself." Profound? Perhaps!

The school looked different today. The smell of floor cleaner is still present, but on this second day, things seem almost quiet. With the exception of the perfunctory "hi," that kids exchange, they just keep to themselves, like robots. Students from each of the four grades go to their respective homerooms. The freshmen are divided into three groups of about twenty each and all three groups march into the library, where Principal Goss is waiting for us. It was time for his famous pep talk to freshmen.

He's a man of average height, powerfully built, in his mid-fifties, with white hair and a face stern enough to strike fear into the hearts of all students and teachers, and maybe sailors as well. He is well-respected in the community for his championship basketball teams that he coached some ten years past, and for his ability to teach mathematics. I thought that his math classes and leadership skills were excellent until some years later when I found out that he ran the school pretty much the way the three richest families in town wanted him to.

Eventually, I came to lose respect for him, as well as for several other town fathers. Nothing extraordinary here; just privileged adults trying to give their children political advantages to compensate for the disadvantages bestowed on their kids through biology and by giving them unearned advantages. The accessories of the rich bring little happiness, either to parent or child. What is real is what counts—the character, accessible to both rich and poor, upon which the accessories are placed. Yet, throughout my high school years, Mr. Goss became a very important though distant adult in my life.

"Welcome to what should be the most important years of your life. You will be judged here by what you do, and your rewards will be seen in your report card. Your report card is your paycheck," he started.

"As young adults, you represent this school and community. It's important to know who you are, so you can be responsible to that identity. You are students, not pupils. Students study, ask questions, and learn. Pupils drift through school. You are also citizens, not subjects. Citizens take on responsibility for their actions and the reputation of their school; subjects are always standing around waiting for someone to tell them what to do.

"By now, most of you know the classes you will be taking. Take them seriously. Today, you have the opportunity to impress teachers and each other by doing a good job. The least that we will accept is that you will show up every day, pay attention, and be respectful. We will demand more, but our demands won't matter unless you act. Start today to take advantage of this opportunity to establish your identity as students and citizens, for it will set in motion your growing reputation. And, that reputation will last a lifetime. Good luck. You are dismissed to go to your first-period classes."

The main academic area of the high school is on one floor. It had four classrooms, the library, the central office, and Mr. Goss's office. The hall or corridor takes up at least one third of the space. To reach the main classrooms, we had to walk up a flight of stairs from the foyer that connects the academic wing with the gym, basement, and outside doorways to the vocational/agriculture buildings.

The building is like a split-level home. The first floor is a half-story up and the basement with the cafeteria, more classrooms, the home economics department, and the toilets and furnace room is only a half-story down. On the east side of the academic wing are three large classrooms: English, mathematics, and general science. The English room is the largest and could be divided into two smaller rooms. The west side includes the library, main science lab, and principal's office.

The hall, which seemed even larger than all of the classrooms put together, has hooks for coats and places below for boots, although only farm kids seemed to wear them even in winter. There were no lockers, and I can't remember anything ever being stolen from anyone. About twenty years later, while playing in an alumni basketball tournament there, I had a wristwatch stolen from the locker room during a game. Things change.

My first class is freshman English with Mr. Kennedy. He acknowledges us as we quietly find and slip into our seats almost afraid to look at one another. Mr. Kennedy has an outline on the board of his course syllabus and tells us that tomorrow, we will all need a notebook in which to write down all of his words of wisdom. It's funny how freshmen don't get irony. He passes out textbooks and begins.

"This is Freshmen English. The point of this year is to have you read and discuss some good literature, learn English grammar, and become a better writer. As you can see from the outline on the board, which you will put in your notebooks tonight, we will read several short stories, one of Shakespeare's plays, one novel, and some of your own writing. We will diagram sentences, take two grammar tests, one at the end of each semester, and write four essays of at least 3,000 words each. Some of this may change if I find that you can handle more. I would like to begin by asking you why you are taking this class."

Tom, a boy I met yesterday at the dentist's office, proclaims, "No choice, we have to be here. It's the law, right?"

"That's the right answer, but it's not a good answer. Does anyone know the difference between a right answer and a good answer?"

This is crazy-making, I think. Aren't good and right the same thing?

"I want you to give right answers, but I am more concerned that you give good answers and know the difference between them. This is one thing that you should learn in Freshman English. Literature should help you discover the good and use it to judge the right. When you get your notebooks, write this in it and ask about it later. Right now, let's get our reading assignment so you can begin your work tonight, and we can begin our work tomorrow."

"The first story we will read this year is *Ivanhoe*, by Sir Walter Scott. It begins on page 14 of your text. This is a tale told by one of the world's great storytellers. It is about chivalry, about Richard the Lionhearted, about love, persecution of Jews, about a corrupt prince, and even about a fellow known as Robin Hood. Ivanhoe is the home of a brave man named Wilfred. He was run off of his land by the prince while he, Wilfred, and the King were off fighting in the Crusades. Does any of this make sense to you? Have any of you heard of any of these people?"

"I heard of Robin Hood," I say. "Saw him in an Errol Flynn movie in Chicago. I liked it a lot."

"Well, Ivanhoe will be even more exciting." Mr. Kennedy promised.

The bell rings for the second period and Mr. Kennedy tells us again to get a notebook and start reading Ivanhoe. "You're dismissed," he ends.

On the way out of Mr. Kennedy's room, Karen approaches me with Allison at her side—crabby, opinionated, pretty Karen. "You should go out for choir. Your voice is, well, it sounds like you could sing. Sign up this week. It's fun too, en'so, Allison?" They laugh and quickly disappear down the hall.

I am already tired and there are still two more classes before lunch—algebra and civics. During lunch I'll walk downtown to buy a notebook from the company store. I had fifteen cents with me and it shouldn't be more than that. Biology and Agriculture are in the afternoon before football practice. Then home to milk cows and do chores, fix some supper, read some Ivanhoe, and go to sleep. Right now, though, I would just focus on the next class taught by Miss Holmes.

Mr. Goss is in the room. He must be substituting for Miss Holmes. She's ill, I guess.

"Let's get started." That command was given by and for him. All of us were ready to start long before he opened his mouth.

"This is algebra, not general math. Some of you may not belong here, but we will find that out in a day or two. You will all need to buy a notebook and there is a text on your desk." Well, I thought, my fifteen cents won't cover two notebooks, and by this afternoon, there might be need for a third or fourth! Maybe the company store will let me charge them. That afternoon, I found out they would.

"We believe that algebra was the invention of a Persian mathematician sometime around 850 AD. The word itself means restoring. All you need to remember is that algebra is the art of restoring the balance between the two sides of an equation, and you do that by subtracting from or adding to one side what has been subtracted from or added to the other.

"Algebra involves symbolic notation. That's a fancy way of saying that we can let a letter like x or y represent any number value we want. In this way, we can make magic seem simple. We do this by putting information into an equation or two, and then reaching a solution by balancing the equation. We take an unknown variable like x and let it represent the unknown quantities of the problem. And if we can construct an equation and then balance it, we are on our way."

I had little or no idea of what he was talking about, but tried to listen harder believing that attention could replace understanding.

"We will first learn how to set up an equation. That is, taking what I say and making an equation out of it. Let me walk you through one."

"Tom, pick a number, write it down, but don't tell me what it is …

Add 15 to it.

Multiply your answer by 3.

Subtract 9.

Divide by 3.

Subtract 8.

"How can we tell the number that Tom started with?" Mr. Goss asks the class.

"After all that adding, multiplying, and subtracting, what's your final answer, Tom? But don't tell us your starting number."

"Thirty-two is my final answer," Tom said.

"Now let's see if we can figure out Tom's starting number. Let x be that number."

"I believe I can do it," I said.

"Come to the board," Goss tells me.

I write the following:

X is the unknown

X ... add 15

X + 15 ... multiply by 3

X + 45 ... subtract 9

X + 36 ... divide by 3

X + 12 ... subtract 8

X + 4 ...

"I need to reach 32, so X must be 28," I say under my breath. "Tom's number is 28," I say a little louder.

"Right answer, but your approach to it is the reason we need to study algebra," Mr. Goss said. "Your reasoning is okay, but without the techniques of algebra, you will never get any better. You will never do college work. Do you believe that?" Goss stopped, went to the board and put the "right"—maybe "good"—answer down.

Pick a number ... X

Add 15 ... X + 15

Multiply by 3 ... $3(X+15) = 3X + 45$

Subtract 9 ... 3X + 36

Divide by 3 ... X + 12

Subtract 8 ... X + 4

X + 4 = 32

X = 28

"Tom's number is 28." I was not sure I got the difference and Goss said nothing more except to read the text.

As class ended, I left the room wondering, not about algebra, but his comment about college. In the back of my mind, I always thought that I would go to college, to play ball if nothing else, but until this moment, I had never really thought about the fact that I couldn't go.

What does he know? Is there some deep inadequacy here, in me, and can I identify it and make it okay?

Maybe Goss is right. I am often cranky, disrespectful of authority, crippled in my relationships with others, especially with girls, envious, of what, I'm not often sure, and retarded in my development to envision a larger world—either on the ball field or in my family. On the other hand, I seem to be at the same level or ahead of my peers in most abilities, and adults seem to like me. I know, however, that there is something wrong.

Eventually, I would come to understand what was, and is still wrong, is the ability to continually forgive—myself included. Perhaps, the forgiveness thing is just a general human inability. The Greeks divided the human soul into three parts: reason, *eros/desire*, and *thymos*, the need for recognition. Reason and desire are clear to me, but *thymos*? Why do we seem to require that others pay attention to us? And, in the pursuit of recognition, why do we find it difficult to forgive others and more importantly, ourselves?

In fact, this need for recognition, often leads to patronization of others, particularly when others disregard us; don't seem to know that we are real people who just want to be noticed. Some adults, who are envious of youth withhold recognition just out of the smallness of their hearts. Maybe this was all that was behind Goss's comment. But teenagers don't or shouldn't care about those kinds of remarks. We have other things on our minds, as I surely did on that day so long ago.

Mr. Norman, our football coach teaches Civics and he gives me a smile as I find a seat in his class. The classroom is in the basement and doubles as part of the cafeteria. Here I feel better. His smile suggests that Coach respects me and believing makes all the difference.

"This is Freshman Civics. We will try to learn what it takes to be a citizen of the nation. We will use, as our text, anything that I find useful, like a Milwaukee newspaper and our local weekly. You can bring in items also. We will study our state and federal constitutions, the Bill of Rights, how and why to participate in government, and questions you might have about your life and times—including, but not limited to, advertising, dating, the Cold War, our future, you name it. But you will be responsible for materials related to your interests. There is a library in the school and one in town; use them," he started.

"Can we interview soldiers?" Allison asked. "I have a cousin who was in the Korean War, and I would love to have him talk to us about being in the Army."

"Why?" Coach questioned.

"Because I can," answered Allison.

"Not a good answer; try again. Write up a reason or rationale for your project and give it to me tomorrow. Tell me how we would all benefit from hearing you cousin, okay?"

"OK," Allison said under her breath.

Coach gives us each a piece of paper with five questions on it. "Please answer these questions as best you can, and when you're finished, hand it in. At that time, you may leave for lunch. If you are eating in the cafeteria, go to the gym until they open the kitchen."

What would you like to know about government?

What can you do to help all of us learn about government?

What kind of government is in this town? In this school? How should I behave in each?

Tell me what government (national, state, or local) is in charge of the following:

- Post office

- Your school

- Streets

- Roads

- Highways

- Radio station

- Court House

- Jail

- Park

- Recreation—fishing, hunting, and boating

- What rights do you have as a citizen? What responsibilities go with each of those rights?

I couldn't finish before the bell sounded. "I am sorry, Coach, but I don't have answers."

"Give me what you have."

I ran downtown, got my notebooks, and made it back to the cafeteria in time to be the last in line.

Lunch—a meal I don't have to fix myself—I love it. Today we had cheeseburgers, mashed potatoes, peas, Jello, and milk. It was all good. I finished just in time for biology.

Mr. Krowe, who always brings his lunch, was just finishing his last bite as the bell rings. We meet in the Agriculture/shop area, as all the science rooms were full this period, a situation Mr. Krowe thought would be resolved next week.

"Biology is the most complex of the sciences. It combines chemistry and physics with art. Let's give it a try. This is the text that you will be using and I have prepared a workbook or notebook for each of you. I want you to look through the book and give me a statement about what you think biology is. What is it that you what to learn? To start, I want to say that I believe we all learn by questioning. So please, ask questions."

"Does biology have anything to do with God or Creation?" Karen questioned. "Are we going to talk about God?"

"No, we're not going to talk about God. Well, maybe a little. Just understand that you cannot learn biology fast. It takes time. If you learn anything here, it should be to develop the behavior of being a critic of yourself, and the way you think and live. If you don't develop a critical mind, you will just go through life, and when you die, you may never have lived."

The class was still; you could have heard a pin drop. No teacher ever talked like this. I didn't know what to make of it. Yes, I want to live, but I had never thought about it. You just live, right? Well, evidently not! There must be a way to understand if you are living. Maybe that's what biology is about—to examine life.

What do I want to learn? I don't know. I knew so little about biology that I just don't know, and the book didn't seem to help. I want to learn about plants, animals, about my body, about sex; I don't know. I just want to know more. I want to understand the regularities and irregularities of nature and of myself. I want to be able to predict what would happen to my body if I do this or that. Can I make myself better through science? I didn't know.

I handed in a page from my new notebook before anyone else with many "I don't know" statements on it.

"Why would you give me this messy piece of paper, Hartoonian? Why would you put your name on something so poorly done? This is not neat. The paper is just ripped out of the notebook. The questions are not well thought out. This is lazy thinking, and you should not put up with it, if for no other reason than you have to put your name on it."

It just wasn't my day. I had one more class before practice; maybe Agriculture would be better.

The Ag wing was its own separate building and today we were already there. We walked in through the classroom and into the large machine shop/garage/chemistry lab. You could tell that this was where the school was putting its resources. The numbers and array of tools and machines was breathtaking.

There were all kinds of projects on display; projects that students had been working on, perhaps all summer. They'd been restoring farm equipment, rebuilding personal cars, and building furniture. I quickly walked back into the classroom and with about thirteen other boys, awaited Mr. Johnson. He seemed to know everyone except me. And there were only three freshmen in his class: Keith, Lee, and me. The rest were all upperclassman and look like, well, like big farmers. I wondered if I belonged there.

"Good afternoon." Johnson starts. He is a short man, maybe five foot five inches, and in his fifties, I guessed. Not a farmer himself, he had, however, made this Chapter of Future Farmers of America (FFA) one of the most respected in the state. His classroom walls were full of trophies attesting to that fact. We all sat down on one side of tables arranged in a U-shape, with Mr. Johnson at his desk at the opening or top of the U. Most of the students looked mature. Even Keith, who was my age, was over six feet tall and seemed like he had been shaving for a year or more. The rest of the guys, mostly juniors and seniors, just look huge to me. I believe that I'm taller than Lee and a couple of the other guys. Big deal!

"We have a full year ahead of us. In addition to your individual projects, I've signed us up for three state competitions. Our first event is soil testing and crop management, which takes place in two weeks at the state college in Stevens Point. I don't expect you freshmen to compete, but do expect you to watch and learn. The second competition is the state speaking contest and there, I expect all of you to enter. Finally, there is my favorite, the team Parliamentary Procedure Contest. We will compete in May, in Madison, against the best FFA programs in the state. Unlike last year, when we finished second, this year, I believe we can win."

He continues. "I would like to spend this first day talking to each of you about the personal project you would like to undertake. Since you upperclassmen have ongoing projects, I'll meet with our three freshmen first." Mr. Johnson came over to our table and began to ask us questions about our responsibilities at home.

"Keith, I know that your family runs one of the largest dairy farms in the county, so I assume that you will want to do something related to that business."

"Well, my brother worked with you five years ago on testing and improving our herd, so I would like to do something else, maybe studying our soil and the application of fertilizers and weed control methods," Keith answered.

"Think about that this week, and let's make a plan by next Monday," Mr. Johnson said in a gentle voice that caught my attention, and Lee's as well. Listening to Mr. Johnson and imagining some possibilities for yourself was exhilarating. I started to feel good about the day.

"Mike, what do you have on your mind?"

"I don't know what I want to do. My first thought is to test milk and learn about dairy or milk production. Sir, I don't know," I answered.

"Well, you need to think about what might be most helpful to you and Happy, as well as the dairy business."

Wow, I thought, he knows about Happy?

Keith and I left the table and went into the lab as Mr. Johnson continued to talk to Lee. We talked about milk and soil testing, but mostly about football practice. The team would have lots of upper classmen on it, and we wondered if we had a chance of making the varsity. There was no junior varsity, as there was in basketball, so it would be hard for us.

We took a fast walk around the shop, checking out the old cars that some of the seniors were working on and thought that we might have the opportunity to build a car—our own car—someday soon.

As we stepped outside, we walked into a beautiful, early fall afternoon. Paying little attention to the beauty of the day, we headed for the gym, knowing that we would be the butt of upperclassmen's jokes.

18

PRACTICE STARTED AT 3:30. KEITH AND I enter the locker room at about 3:15 and are "greeted" by members of the team in a tone that echoed like drill sergeants. "…freshmen…we're looking forward to some good ass-kickin'," as Keith and I tried to look even smaller and figure out how to put on our pads.

I had to face that fact that these guys could hurt me. I was terrified. They had hair on their chests and legs. I, on the other hand, had little or none. As a matter of fact, there were even other freshmen bigger than Keith. Tim, John, and Jerry were about my size, but their muscles were well defined.

My growth would eventually come. In a year, I would grow to the height of five foot ten, but remain skinny. Right now, I knew this was going to be a hard day. I had never played football, but I desperately wanted to—to be one of the guys. In high school, we were judged by our grade age. A freshman is not a senior, except some are.

Why do we label kids by age, particularly those who want to play ball? Regardless of physical maturity, you're told that you will play in the 14- or 16-year-old age group. Chronological age is everything. If we really paid attention to the fact that young men and women develop their physical maturity at different rates, we would be more flexible in the way we classify athletes.

Anyone who has been around athletes between the ages of ten and eighteen knows well the physical differences that exist among youth of the same age. Some parents actually keep their boys (and it is mostly boys) home an extra year or two so they will have the size to play football or hockey in high school. This all evens out at about age eighteen or twenty, but it's rough on those of us who are late physical bloomers.

Many students who could have had great sports experiences in high school never get the chance because coaches often won't see the kids' potential. It is the case that boys born in January or February have a better chance of making the team than boys born in July or August. They are simply six months older.

In 1953, if the smaller male athlete was to shine, he had to show much more heart and brains than the bigger players. So, in that moment, I made up my mind that I would be noticed, first for my hustle, and next, by my ability to understand the game in all its subtleties. Coaches, Happy, the cows, or whoever, would not get in my way. Of course, they couldn't; I was the only one capable of that. I wish that I had known the real power of that thought right there, right then.

We began practice in full gear with all of us in four lines and the coach and captain from last year, Roger Younger, leading our warm-up exercises. Stretching, then running in place, jumping-jacks, up-and-downs, sit-ups, and push-ups. We had no weight room. I don't believe that there was a set of weights in the whole school. Back then coaches believed that lifting weights would make you muscle-bound and slow you down. Since most of the players did heavy farm work, perhaps weights were unnecessary. Practice would take care of the rest of our training. Next, we ran four one-hundred-yard sprints—two times up the field and two times back. I finished somewhere in the middle of the pack, feeling more winded than I thought I should.

Then we started some "light" hitting drills. The drill I was assigned to had two of us standing face to face, about ten feet apart, while one of the managers dropped a football between us. The point was for one of us to pick up the ball, me, for example, before the other guy, which I almost always did. With the ball tucked under my arm, the other guy tried to tackle me—or, in this case, just knock the crap out of me. Since I usually got the ball, I usually got the crap knocked out of me.

The drill I liked best was the one when the manager just gave the ball to one runner and the runner would try to get by two tacklers. I did it twice, so afraid of being hit I ran with terror through and away from all tacklers. We also went through several blocking drills. After about a half hour, Coach called us up to talk to us about the offense and defenses we would use this year. By that time, though, every part of my body was hurting; but for some strange reason, I felt almost good about hitting and being hit, and being here on the field.

Our offense was called a "short-punt." Coach said that it is a variation on the Single Wing, only with a balanced line. Balanced line just meant that the center had a guard and tackle on his right and a guard and tackle on his left. One of the ends could be split five to fifteen yards from the tackle, or they both could stay in tight, next to the tackle.

In the backfield, the quarterback was not "under" center, but lined-up behind the right guard, and served mostly as the signal caller and a blocking back. The most important "back" was the tailback, who lined up deep, seven yards right behind the center. The ball was centered directly to him, "leading" the tailback in the direction in which he would move. For example, as the quarterback barked, "Hut-one, hut-two, hut-three," the ball would be centered on "three." On that count, the tailback would step and turn to his right and take one or two steps as the ball came to him on the run. If he was quick enough, he could reach top speed in about three or four steps and from that position, could run off-tackle or around end. He could also pass or punt, thus the name short-punt, I guess.

The right halfback and fullback lined up three to five yards behind the line and their jobs consisted of blocking for the tailback, going out for passes, or running counter (direction) plays. Those are plays that start to the right and come back to the left. Sometimes the ball was centered directly to a halfback or fullback and he could run right up the "holds" between the center and guard, and sometimes even off tackle.

In the short-punt formation, counters served a similar purpose to a reverse. While the short punt did not have the flexibility of the "T" offenses, where the quarterback takes the ball directly from center, its strength was in its power runs. If people could block, the defense would be overwhelmed. It was like seeing a small army coming right at you, as the tailback would not only have a line blocking for him, but a pulling guard, a quarterback, a halfback, an end, and if the defense didn't adjust, four yards were relatively easy to get.

Coach talked us through the finer points of the offense by literally dragging players by the shoulders or shirt, without regard for their feelings, into positions in the line or backfield, particularly when he wanted to explain something in greater detail. He gave us all playbooks and told us to memorize the thing by the next day.

Easy for upper classmen, I thought, but to us freshmen, it's all new and I have other homework and chores to do. And, besides, I am tired, my lip is bleeding, and I have bruises all over my arms and legs from the tackling drills. I wondered if I really could play football.

"Tomorrow we'll talk about our defense, and by Thursday, we will start to fill positions. Think about what you can contribute to this team. Now, give me two laps around the field and get out of here. Don't forget to shower!"

19

THE BUS RIDE HOME SEEMS FAR TOO SHORT. Not enough time to think about the day. Perhaps, I just didn't want to go home. Even today, these many years later, that feeling strikes me like a cold chill. Happy will be letting the cows in the barn and getting ready for milking. I would like to eat something before I join him, but that will have to wait.

I wished that Mark were here, but he had left with Mama for Chicago some two weeks ago. I miss him so much that I almost start crying. Crying, perhaps, not just about his absence, but also about my situation. Mark is fine, I think. He's living with our half-brother, Joe and his wife, in an apartment within walking distance of the elementary school that he's attending. Funny, not a word from Mark or Mama. But he's doing fine. At least that's what I believed. I won't see him for any length of time until next spring. By then, he would look skinny, his hair will be far too long, and his eyes will look quiet and hungry. My brother—I hardly knew him. Things will get better, I thought, when Mark returns. It's a hope I cling to.

The chores are done in a zombie-like manner. I am so tired and I hurt. All I want to do is sleep, so I inhale a bowl of Cheerios and go to bed. I read for maybe ten minutes. Sleep defeats Ivanhoe.

Happy calls up to me at 5:00. "Time to get up. It's daylight in the cedar swamp." Happy is trying to be funny. The cedar swamp is very thick and it takes until mid-morning before the morning sun lights up the swamp's surface. Rolling out of bed in the dark, I step into the clothes I took off last night. I could swear that they were still warm. After milking, a quick shower, and a breakfast of eggs, ham, milk, and bread, I am back on the bus ready for my third day of school, with none of my homework finished. I have to find a different way of doing things.

Football practice starts this afternoon, the same way it did yesterday, with running, exercises, and hitting drills; sorry, blocking and tackling drills. Then Coach brings us together, all twenty-three of us, to listen to the subject of defense.

"Because of the personnel we have this year and the fact that Roger is one of the best players in the conference, we are going to play a diamond and one on defense."

From my freshman vantage point, Roger is a hell of a man. About six feet tall and 200 pounds, he just looks like a football player, the kind you would see in a magazine. He was good at football, basketball, and baseball. He had been the tailback for the last two seasons, and would start there this year. Coach said he would also play linebacker. In those days, most of us would play both ways—offense and defense.

In this defensive set, Roger would be our only linebacker. He would back up the whole line by himself. At the time, I didn't know just how exceptional that was.

"We will have a six-man line. No nose guard; their center will be left uncovered; our two guards will play off the inside shoulders of the offensive guards; our two tackles will also play off the inside shoulders of the offensive tackles; and our two defensive ends will play three yards outside our tackles, but adjusting with the position of the offense end or halfback."

Coach placed six people on the line, guys he thinks might play those positions. "Behind the line, Roger will be our linebacker. Roger will also call our defensive formations."

He told Roger to stand three yards in front of the un-covered center. "You are our linebacker, the one in our diamond and one. From here, Roger, you can read the center and quarterback, and you are free to roam up and down the line, depending on where you think the play is going. About five yards behind Roger, but more committed to staying home; that is, protecting the middle area or zone against run or pass, is the first point of our diamond. This man reacts to the play and to Roger, plugging any hole too large for Roger and the line, and backing up when reading pass. Bert, for now, you take that spot," Coach directs.

"Five yards deeper, behind our diamond point man, Bert, and outside our defensive ends, we'll have two defensive cornerbacks; Jack, you and Martin fill those positions. Finally, we have the safety, making up the deep point of the diamond, about twelve to fourteen yards off the line of scrimmage. Leroy, try it back there."

A diamond and one. Seemed like it should be one and a diamond. I didn't understand yet. I guess we have one man backing up the line with four others forming the four points of the diamond, perhaps moving like a zone defense in basketball. The "one" was Roger. The diamond included Bert, Jack, Martin, and Leroy. I don't know why the conception was troubling to me; I guess I would understand better if I had the diagrams in my head. If I ever get a chance, I'll read the playbook. That should help.

Arriving home at 5:30, I changed into barn clothes and greeted Happy, who has already started milking. I was feeling a little healthier than yesterday and would make and eat a better dinner tonight.

I just can't get over the feeling of being alone. Maybe being alone is okay. In fact, solitude may be an elixir for loneliness. I comforted myself in that thought as I established a place in my bedroom, reading both the football playbook and Ivanhoe. This established place will become my home within the house.

I found an old, faded, and rough board table in the small bedroom and dragged it into my bedroom. It would serve as a desk for both Mark and me. A workable table lamp, the kind people use in their living rooms, would be my desk lamp, and I take one of our wooden dining room chairs—we have six—for my desk chair. A few books, an old beer mug as a pen/pencil holder, and a view of the fields and woods beyond, make for a great thinking place.

It's a place I would return to throughout my life simply by giving every future desk, home or office, these same attributes of light, mug, and, whenever possible, a view. I still remember the questions I received from college classmates and professional colleagues; "Why do you use a table lamp on your desk?"

"I love the soft glow given by the large shade. The office looks better for it, don't you think?" I would reply, and, of course, to me, it did.

Friday is here before I'm ready for it. A week into my freshman year and it seemed as though the world had become more complex and interesting. My perception of myself was changing. I was beginning to play again. I was learning to enjoy my body once again.

Perhaps, it was just the notion that the hungry soul sees everything as sweet. Well, if life seems sweeter today, it may have something to do with school, or it may just be that my appetite for things and comfort is starting to fit this landscape of which I am becoming a part.

For those of us boys on athletic teams, physical education was not a requirement. It was, however, for everyone else— every girl, of course. On Fridays, phy-ed was co-ed, and every boy, especially the athletes, wanted to participate.

Phy-ed on Fridays meant dancing. I was terrified of dancing and of girls, but since I could join in, I did. The thought of being close to girls was, well, thrilling. They smelled good, and most wore skirts that would be lifted by the air as they spun around, exposing their lower legs, and sometimes, even their knees. Wow!

It seems that dancing and athletics are two ways you can develop a reputation. I believe, in part, that this reputation is created by what you believe others are imagining about you if you do them well. Be that as it may, I danced, and it was joyful, reputation notwithstanding.

On this first Friday, my mind was sort of numb. We are to have our first football scrimmage and with only enough players for both offence and defense, it was clear that freshmen will be used, and I mean used. I had no idea if Coach would use me on offence or defense, both, or not at all. I only knew some of the offence plays and less about our defense.

Back to Ivanhoe ... Mr. Kennedy talked about the friendships among the characters in the story. We saw that family relationships are no assurance of friendship, as witnessed by Richard the Lionhearted and his brother, Prince John.

"What is a friend?" Mr. Kennedy asks.

"A friend is someone who helps you, someone you can really talk to ... someone who understands you?" Allison says in question form.

"Of course, that's right, but the good answer is something else."

Oh, no. Not that again; the right answer is never enough for him.

"A friend IS someone who helps you, who understands you, and someone you can count on, without the expectation of reward," Kennedy said.

"But how is your answer right as well as GOOD?" I asked.

"The good has to do with how your identity is connected to virtue. The good is universal; it is always true. Good is beyond our ability to measure. It's what you do for others because of what is inside you, and the action MUST be done, with no thought of reward, honor, notoriety, or even safety. It's what a good person does.

Mr. Kennedy continues. "Take the man who plows his sick neighbor's field even without the neighbor's knowledge or request or incentive. Or the woman who helps a child to read without any thought of reward ... or the person who goes into a burning building to save another human being and is killed. These are examples of the good, of friendship. You help without regard to earthly or heavenly reward. You do the good thing, because that's who you are, period."

Now I truly was confused.

I'm still not sure of his meaning of friendship. How often have I done or even said something I thought was "good" and later felt ridiculous? Maybe I just did the right thing, not the good. Sometimes, I don't know what the right or good thing to do is. Maybe he meant that your REASONS for doing something for others, not the doing itself—which any machine can do—can lead to ridicule or courage. But if you have consciousness, if you are consistent with your identity, you will do the good thing.

No, that doesn't make sense. What if you are a bad or stupid person? If the good is universal, then it must be beyond me, the individual. I must be engaged with a virtue that can be shared by all people, those alive, those dead, and those yet to be born. The good is a constant in an ever-changing moral landscape. Perhaps, the right varies with time, place, and culture. Maybe, doing the right thing involves rewards, or at least, the avoidance of shame, while doing the good thing simply confirms you to God, or eternity, and informs the nature of your conscience. I don't know. I think that Allison's answer makes enough sense for me.

This is what I love about being in class—a chance to play at thinking, and to have a real conversation. But before I know it, it's that time. I move quickly to the locker room to get ready for football practice. Passing through the gym, I notice several boys shooting baskets and I think, I wish that I could just do that instead of getting beat up on the football field.

As Mr. Kennedy might say, that's not you; it's not your identity. Waking swiftly by, I receive a high pass from Lee, who didn't go out for football, inviting me to take a shot. I jump to catch the ball with a beautiful synthesis of mind, eyes, hands, and legs; my whole body feels in harmony. I loft a long shot toward the basket as I continue toward the locker room.

There's a wonderful certainty and amazement when you know the shot is true; your hands, feet, and the ball go just where they should. Sometimes it goes in, sometimes not. Either way, it's a feeling that those who have never played a sport will never experience. I do know that these experiences will pass, but to never have had them, well, that would be cruel, indeed. It is the ultimate separation of mind, body, and soul.

Unlike the equally wonderful acts of enjoying music, observing the beauty of the mountains, or the sight of a red sunrise, these expressions of physical harmony are the hallmarks of youth. And they will be missed, big time. But if wise, we will see these declines as the freeing of our souls. I think that this is really life's trade-off for the fortunate, and it is the essence of being earthly and mortal, and in relationship with yourself.

Back to reality. This is a big day. We are suited up in red and green vests; green for offense; red for defense. I was given a green vest. Great, I thought, I know the offense better and won't look like such an idiot.

After the same warm-up exercises, Coach lines us up along the line of scrimmage and puts me in at the right halfback's position. I try to remember. First, I need to know the numbering system. That is, the offensive line has numbered "holes" in it. The center is 0. The holes to his right are even numbers: 2, inside the tackle; 4, off tackle; 6, around end. The holes to the center's left are odd numbers 1, 3, 5. The backs are also numbered. The quarterback is number 1, right halfback is number 2 (my number), the fullback is number 3, and the tailback is number 4. If the play number is 44, it just means that the tailback will run right, off tackle. It's all so logical on paper. In addition to the numbering system, the next most important thing to figure out is who to block so the running back can actually run.

For some strange reason, at least I think so, Coach huddled us up and calls 33, fullback off tackle to the left. It's a counterplay, and my job was to block the right defensive end out so the fullback could cut off of my butt. The ball was centered directly to the fullback, he took a step to his right, this movement will allow the blocking to set-up, then he will cut back to his left, breaking off my block and running down field—all this is theory, of course.

"On two, break," Coach says.

At the line, the quarterback starts his count, "Hut one; hut two." The ball is centered to the fullback; he steps right and cuts back to his left, looking for my block. I stay low, looking for the end so I might take him out of the play. He is perhaps our biggest player, but I don't see him. He, on the other hand, sees the fullback and creams him at the line … no gain.

Before I could turn around and head back to the huddle, Coach was right in my face. "What the hell was that, Hartoonian? Block the end, that's how the play is designed … you block out the end … what's your problem? Where's your head? Can't you read?"

"Yes sir, I can read. The end is supposed to come straight across the line, about two yards into the backfield. It's right in the play book. He didn't. So, there was no one for me to block."

"What? What the hell do you mean; there's always someone to block." His nose and mouth were now so close, I could smell his nasty cigarette breath.

"Do you think that the end is going to just come over the line and let you block him? Do you think he's as dumb as you? You have to find and destroy him, before you're destroyed. And if you can't find the end, God damn it, hit somebody wearing a different color."

"But sir, the play is written just the way I played it." I said in a voice I didn't think he could hear and wished he hadn't.

"Let me tell you something, and you'd all better hear this; football ain't played on paper, it's played on grass. You react to what's going on in front of you, not something written in the book...THINK! Run another play."

The second play was 44 ... tailback off right tackle. My job on this play, as I remember it, was to get to hole 4 before the tailback and "clean out" any defensive lineman or linebacker as the fullback blocked the left defensive end. Roger should run off of the fullback's butt and behind me to run free beyond the line of scrimmage.

Of course, all these guys seemed twice as big as me and as I got to the hole, I was the one hit—hit twice, once high by the linebacker and low by the defensive tackle. I didn't clean out the hole, I clogged up the hole. Roger fell over me, and my calf muscle was hit so hard that I am afraid to stand on it.

"Hartoonian, do you really what to play football? You are stinking up my field. Give it up before you get yourself killed. Ron, get in here. Hartoonian, take your sorry ass off the field and think about whether you want to play or are even capable of playing. This is no place for a little city boy."

I began to limp back toward the locker room, crying. I wasn't sure if the tears were from the pain in my calf or the worse pain from his words. I just hurt, badly. I had no one to turn to; even Coach thought me worthless.

Jesus, I was thinking like a God-damned victim. I could decide to recover and grow, or I could just consider myself a piss-ant. I didn't know what I had inside me. But I couldn't think about it now. All I know is I'm here; again, with myself. Coach said today, "Block, so Roger can see and run to daylight" I, on the other hand, will have to make daylight.

I wanted to play ball, but I must confess that at times, I just wanted to watch. Right now, this may be one of those times. Looking back at the beginning of my freshman year from the distant future, it seems so clear how important advice from a loved one is or could be. Not that a fourteen-year-old would take advice from anyone, but he ought to have the pleasure of rejecting it. No such contentment was in store for me.

20

AN EARLY FALL WEEKEND IN DAIRYLAND is filled with work. The second crop of hay must be safely stored and every foot of space in the hay loft accounted for so we would have enough feed for the cows until they return to the pastures in spring. Happy said that some years, when the rains were inadequate, he had to buy hay from other farmers, sometimes from as far away as Iowa. When that happens, the hope of any profit for the year disappears.

The milking area of the barn had to be white-washed before winter; machines no longer in service had to be cleaned and stored in the machine shed; firewood for the furnace had to be hauled and stacked in the basement; apples were wrapped in newspaper and put into barrels and, in turn, placed in the basement along with potatoes and onions that were stored on shelves in the dark area of the basement.

There were also persistent everyday tasks on top of these. Every weekend, the milking machines and pipes had to be washed in an extra-special way, and the milk house was completely washed with disinfectant.

This was also the time of the year when we butchered a hog or two, and a year-old, castrated bull calf that would soon be joined in the freezer by wild game such as pheasants, squirrels, and venison. For me, the week's end was also time for grocery shopping and cleaning the house. I'm using the term loosely as the only rooms that were cleaned were the kitchen, bathroom, and once a month, my bedroom—I never went into Happy's bedroom.

Some weeks it was impossible to accomplish all of this so we made choices, however, that always put the cows first. And, I always tried to make time to do something with friends, maybe Keith or Tom. We'd go to one of the last drive-in movies of the season or bowling. Or, maybe we'd just go to the drive-in for some jukebox music, a burger, and malt.

It's Saturday night, and we wouldn't have a TV at home for another two years, and besides the weather is still glorious.

What's nice about fall on the North Coast—the category "Midwest" doesn't fit Wisconsin, most of northern and eastern Minnesota, and Michigan—is the weather. I'm talking about those few precious days from the first frost until the first snow. It's what's called "Indian Summer" for what reason I'm not sure. Days are bright, clear, and pleasantly cool. Nights are illuminated with stars that seem to appear in magnitudes not recognized before the first frost. And the colors—the hardwood forests of maples, butternuts, and oaks are punctuated by low swamplands and streams displaying groves of cedars, tamaracks, and poplars. The gold, reds, browns, greens, together with the blue of the sky and white fluffy clouds, make a visual banquet for anyone who cares to look or listen.

Not as expansive as the Great Plains to our west, the steep hills and forests of northeastern Wisconsin tend to hold your sight close and focus it on such things as the stone walls that line the winding roadsides, or the red barns with silos, and black-and-white cows grazing nearby.

By late September, a hint of frost after breakfast mixes with the dew and creates a jeweled world. On such fall Saturdays, it's not difficult to get out of bed at 4:30 a.m. to attend the arrival of the morning star. The warmth, solitude, and beauty of this precious mixture of frost, dew, and crystal sky seem to extend in every direction, touching every blade of grass, every leaf, every stone, and every soul.

Besides the weather, the notion of "Midwesterner" doesn't fit the people of this region either. The settlement patterns were unique in the sense that people came from all over the world and in a sequence that provided a powerful texture and mosaic.

First, this is Indian land. The Menominee word Wisconsin means 'gathering of waters.' Wisconsin was the land of the crossroads of Native Americans and the French fur traders resulting in early European commerce. Later, it became a land for displaced Indians because of the commerce. Maps of Wisconsin before and after the Civil War show a demographic of diverse Native density unmatched in the United States. The federal government continued to resettle Indians here well into the late 19th century. The Stockbridge-Muncie, who were the last of the Mohegans, and the Menominee, who lost most of their lands to European settlers, were students in our high school. The Native people had their lands taken, yet provided a rich diversity not well understood then, perhaps, not even today.

Many people came here from Virginia and several Border States, like Tennessee and Kentucky before the Civil War, escaping the institution of slavery. Many enslaved people journeyed to this Free State and became prosperous farmers in the southwestern regions of the state.

People came from New England and New York, setting up stores and factories. From Germany, Sweden, Norway, England, Wales, and later from Italy, Poland, and Greece they came, to escape poverty and experience freedom. They came to create wealth for their families and enriched the country. They brought with them ideas of religious tolerance, at least for those who understood God as they did, hard work, the importance of education, and notions of government that made this region just different. By the time John Kennedy was elected President of the United States in 1960, the city of Milwaukee had had Socialists mayors for more years than it had Democratic or Republican leaders.

People point to the high quality of life in this region today, or at least until recent years. What they are pointing at is the quality of the infrastructure or commonwealth. It's good because those early settlers had a strong belief in education. And, because they were determined, they stayed steadfast in their interaction with this often harsh, but, more often, beautiful landscape leaving a legacy of commitment. These and many other combinations of people, ideas, landscapes, and values made for a diverse and interesting place. To me, however, it seemed that there was always something just under the surface that was uneasy to this outsider.

Anyway, whatever it is, the "North Coast" is not the "Midwest." The North Coast was something different, something more diverse, and something more beautiful. Perhaps it was a place where people would dare to think more critically.

21

NIGHTS COME EARLIER NOW; THE COWS are milked in twilight, and Saturday-night-out with the boys will, indeed, seem short. I call Keith and he is just finishing chores too, so I ask if his older brother, Leland—Lee, that is—can drive us to town for an hour or so; maybe just to the drugstore for a soda or malt, look around and come home.

"If he can't, I'll ask Happy," I say. Keith calls back in three minutes. In those days, we were on a party line. That meant that all six or eight farm families in the area were on the same line with equal access to your call. They could listen in on your conversations and you on theirs. All incoming calls were distinguishable by the RING. Our ring was two shorts and a long. Using proper phone etiquette, you only picked up when your phone rang its special ring.

Keith tells me that Lee will drive us to town, and he also wants to do some bowling. Great! I've had enough of the farm for one day and I can already taste the strawberry malt. It would be nice to bowl tonight and see the inside of the place and meet some of the "town" boys who hang out there. I get cleaned up— quick bath, clean jeans, and a sweatshirt—and I'm ready in ten minutes. In fifteen, Lee and Keith are driving around the yard light to pick me up.

Lee graduated from high school four years ago and married his high school sweetheart. "Had to," Keith told me later; perhaps ten percent of our high school classmates would fall into that category. He and Marion lived on the family farm with Keith and their mother and father.

Keith's father, Luther, was as harsh and quiet a person as I had ever met. He never seemed to talk and his actions toward me were always emotionless. It was as though I were invisible. But then again, invisibility may be a common condition one is obligated to carry simply because of being different. One might think that being different would make an individual stand out, maybe in a good way; but here in rural Wisconsin in the early 1950s, an individual who stands out because of some external trait is, indeed, not present at all.

Full humanity is simply denied because what they believe around here is the exceptionality of Northern European lineage and farmer "distinction." Denial, or not seeing, is a huge factor in our history, as well as in our propensity to discriminate. We pretend that we don't see differences. We don't, because we make the difference disappear; we deny its existence. It's not colorblindness; it's simply blindness that makes the other invisible.

Thus, we deny ourselves many experiences and insights. As it is, it seems that much of our life is spent making the conscious decisions not to know, and in that innocence, we fail to realize what life could really be. Que sera, sera is our motto, as though there were some God-given master plan that we should follow. But as Shakespeare suggested, the fault comes not from above, but from deep within ourselves. Perhaps from our communities as well.

I found this exceptionality missing in Keith's mother, Hannah, who was the earth mother. She loved without knowing who, without knowing how, without knowing why. There was nothing planned or calculated in her presence, her manner, or speech.

I met her for the first time some two weeks before school started. It was on a Friday morning. The night before, she called and asked if I wanted to come over for breakfast, after chores, and go into town with her and Keith to get a pre-school haircut. Breakfast! The thought of having someone else preparing breakfast was such a pleasant thought. "Yes," I said in a heart-beat.

And come Friday morning, I was at their door before my hair was dry from the morning shower. The breakfast was wonderful. We had pancakes, eggs and bacon, and hot chocolate milk. Everything was perfect. The pancakes were golden brown. The homemade butter, submersed in local pure maple syrup, turned each bite into waves of flavor that I can still summon to this day. The gentle taste of the hot chocolate milk continued warming my mind as we drove toward town. How great it is to start the morning this way. How great to have a mother, even if the present father wasn't so great. After that day, I always thought the world of Keith's mother. Keith wasn't so bad, either.

Keith, Lee, and I made it to town in about fifteen minutes. Lee parked near the drugstore, which was in the middle of town, located directly across Main Street from the barbershop, which was adjacent to the bowling alley. Even at 7:30 in the evening, the store was crowded with kids of all ages, as well as many adults getting prescriptions filled, looking at greeting cards, or just talking.

Finding no empty tables in the drugstore at which to sit, malts in hand, the three of us moved outside into a busy Saturday-night scene and went next door to sit down on the bench in front of the hardware store. We just sat there in silence enjoying our drinks and watching people walk and drive by. Mostly we observed town girls; I suspect even married Lee looked, too.

The early fall evening was cool, yet every once in a while, a warm breeze touched our faces, adding to the delight of the moment, and belying the fact that any morning now a killing frost would cover the landscape.

When you spend a day focused on farm chores, seeing and speaking with few people, even a bustling, though small, town in Wisconsin can seem like an exotic city. The Company General Store, the hardware store, the Chevy car dealership, the one clothing/shoe store in town, and the several bars were now receiving the many farmers and some of the townspeople who turned the place into a commercial boom every weekend.

This was not a quiet street or sidewalk. Cars and pickup trucks were everywhere. Some older high school boys drove their fathers' cars up and down Main Street, looking for people to look at them. Men and women argued in front of the bars about the Cold War, the price of milk, how the high school football and basketball seasons would go, and whether or not home games should be played on Friday or Saturday nights.

The merchants didn't want people at ballgames when they should be in their stores shopping; they disagreed as to whether more people would come to town if the games and shopping occurred on the same night or on different nights. The tradition was to have folks come to town on all three days of the weekend: Friday nights for games, Saturday nights for shopping, and Sundays for church. "Don't mess with a good thing," was the general attitude. But those attitudes were changing, and rapidly.

Even in northern Wisconsin, the world was at our door. Every day there was news about civil rights, and how Negros in the South were being discriminated against, abused, and not treated like citizens. We didn't know the half of it. There was fear of the atom bomb. There was the news that the Russians would take over our country and the world if we didn't become more responsible regarding our knowledge of the world and our selfish ways.

Some believed that we were getting too soft—obviously they had never worked on a dairy farm. We had too many consumer goods. We had lost our way as Americans. And, we were being manipulated by the government in Washington, by advertisers in New York, and we were not getting the education we needed to keep us free and prosperous. And, the newspapers suggested that Americans were wasting too much time watching TV.

Change was all around us, but for me, and perhaps for most high school students, it was enough to make it through the day. "Work hard, work smart, and the future will be your oyster." That was the unspoken message of the school and community. And the spoken shout: "Beat Boulder City on Friday."

We finished our drinks, walked across the street, and entered the bowling alley. From the door, four lanes were visible across the large foyer. There was a counter on the left for checking out shoes, a soft drink and snack food bar in the middle of the foyer, and restrooms to the right. The place smelled of fried food and sweeping compound with a hint of old shoe leather that became more pronounced as you approach the check-in counter.

Lee asked if we could bowl a line. "Not for about a half hour or so." The guy behind the counter is Kurt Meyers, a senior at school with a reputation for being a very good basketball player and a sort of goof-off around town. That said, he has this great job and instructs everyone on the finer points of the game of bowling, whether they want the advice or not. He is about five-foot-ten, and has hair that is almost white, with skin to match.

I found him mysterious in appearance and it was hard for me to stop staring at him. He was perhaps not much different in looks from others around here, towheads all, but where I came from, his extreme lightness would have instigated interesting comments.

Lee decided we didn't have the half hour or so to wait, so we watched a few minutes and left. No fries, no pop, and no good-byes. We walked back down Main Street a few yards to where Lee parked and drove up Main Street one last time before going home, hoping to catch a glimpse of some excitement or town gossip—a hope that faded quickly with each passing street light. Maybe we believed that something or someone would reach out and stop us from leaving the lights of town before entering the darkness of the road, fields, and forests beyond.

This fall evening seemed particularly dark, and upon reaching our driveway, the darkness made me feel as though my eyes had failed me. Using my feet as much as my eyes, I carefully stepped toward the back door, all the while becoming more anxious.

The inside of the house was even darker than the night. As I felt my way across the kitchen, I could hear snoring coming from Happy's bedroom which added to the ghostly atmosphere. Walking faster now, I made my way up the stairs, three at a time, to my bedroom, feeling all the while that there was someone or something else waiting in the darkness. Once through the bedroom door, I quickly turned on the desk lamp. The intensity of the light unnerved me even more than the dark. I felt naked in the abrupt illumination, so I turned it off, quickly undressed, and jumped into bed. Covers over my head; sleep came, but with a chill.

22

SUNDAY MORNING WAS COOL AND THE dawn came slowly. We were almost finished with breakfast before the sunlight finally chased all the shadows from the driveway and backyard.

"I think we should go to church today," I blurted out for some unknown reason. It wasn't last night's fear of the dark and I wasn't trying to invoke religion into breakfast. I had no spirit of meanness. I was not, in any conscious way, bringing the fear of the Lord into Happy's life, even though we both knew that he drank to the point of being alcoholic. Happy was married, but alone. I somehow knew that. Alone. Me too. But I simply longed to engage with others rather than spend a long, quiet day with Happy. I needed to have some contact with people who had ideas to discuss, peculiar or not, about things beyond cows and cow shit.

There is a theology of farming complete with immutable laws and life-altering judgments about the nature of good and bad agriculture. The life of a dairy farmer with its necessary strict adherence to the good of the cow is a religion in itself. Intricate, rigid, and often mysterious, it was sowing the seeds of its own destruction even as we worshiped in the church we called "the barn." The small dairy farm was becoming ever more out of step with the economic realities of the day; but we just didn't know anything else—the demands of this bovine religion forbid us from seeing far. This, of course, is the formula for disaster—being stuck in time. It sounds like the definition of hell, and hell happens to us here on earth when we choose not to see beyond our present circumstances.

God, farming, consuming—they're all about beliefs, faith, meaning, and habits. The methods of the discipline of theology are important to the farmer, but only when combined with observations and experimentation. Farmers know that science can only take them so far, and too soon, they need to look beyond and behind what their eyes can see. However, from time to time, our faith dominates our reason to the point of natural blindness, and we become sitting ducks to any right-sounding fad or scam. There are, indeed, all kinds of theologies in our minds and around us all the time, each with its own sacred text, saints, prophets, devils, and doctrines that define the state of our reality. The secret is to play science off of faith, and faith off of science.

When faith is not held up to reflection and experimentation, things like marriage, baseball, war, the economy, and institutions expose their pathologies. And, of course, the same can be said about science. The dairy farmer needed something to tell him and the world that shoveling shit is sacred, transcendent, and purposeful. But the farmer so entrenched in that belief will not see the future coming.

Rigid theologies, of course, become righteous-making, and, whenever possible, we should avoid righteousness and righteous people; those who think themselves always on God's side. They will make your life a living hell. They are without grace, without happiness, and without life. They know little of religious history and less of God. Thinking themselves better than the rest, they add little to the community but resentment and anger.

I guess I didn't really know if Happy was caught up in this kind of thinking, as I believed most people were here, young and old alike. Many seemed so aged in spirit even while physically young. Growth seemed out of the question, yet without it, beauty and knowledge are no longer of value. It seemed that people here didn't reflect on their behavior or the world because they were certain about everything. Who needs knowledge and beauty anyway? Having said that, however, it was clear that they did understand self-organized order, from helping each other with field work to starting a cooperative, community-owned hospital.

Now I wanted something else, something beyond cow religion, something more substantial. I didn't want my spirit killed by fixed beliefs that are creators of cynicism and shame, and destroyers of happiness. My intention was to find out about theologies from the horse's mouth. Go to church with an open mind and spend some time with my peers. Perhaps, not the best of reasons for church going, but it was all I had, and besides, the Lutheran church was the place where the pretty girls worshiped.

So, I said again, "Let's go to church."

"Not me." Happy said. "I haven't been to church in forty years and I don't intend to break my record today."

"Well, will you take me into town?"

"No. Call Luther, Keith's dad; they always go to church—the rich Lutheran church. Not that it improves his sour face. All he ever thinks about is himself. You go with them."

"I want to go to the small church." I said, thinking about my rationale of pretty girls.

"Well, maybe you can go with Charlie and Sarah. They go to the little Lutheran church."

"Good idea!"

Charlie and Sarah are neighbors who live a half mile to our south. They have no children. They lost a son who died of birth defects and since then Sarah and Charlie have been depressed most of the time. Charlie? Well, Charlie is one of those men born in the wrong century. I always saw him as a cowboy or sailor or army officer living in the 19th century. Thin as a rail, yet strong in arm and countenance, he commanded respect from others for his skill around animals and machines. I always had the feeling, however, that other men thought of him as a little off-putting, and I saw him as unhappy.

Sarah was beautiful, I thought, or once had been. Sarah had ashen-blue eyes and a face that was easygoing, but only when she smiled. Without her smile, her eyes went dead and she became unpleasant. Happy was right about church; they went every week and to the little church. I called, and they said that they would be happy to have me join them.

I washed up and put on a clean shirt and the one pair of dress pants I had. I would not own a new sport coat until the end of my freshman year of college, and that was a navy blazer awarded to me for winning a letter in baseball. From time to time, Mama did bring home some shirts, pants, and even a suit she was given when she worked at Fields in Chicago's Loop during the Christmas rush. These were clothes on display or on mannequins that had become soiled.

The day was still cool and sunny as we arrived for the 10 o'clock service. The earlier service was in German, but this would be in English. People still carried on conversations in German around here. Happy subscribed to a German newspaper published in Milwaukee.

It was a small church and an unadorned service. There were fifty or sixty adults and children in attendance. Sunday school was conducted between the 8 and 10 o'clock services and worship would end at 11 o'clock or 11:15 so everyone could be back home by noon. The Lutheran services were wonderful to listen to, particularly the music and sermons. This Sunday's lesson was about the chosen people—Israel. Or was it about us, here and now?

You are a people holy to your God; Yahweh,
Your God has chosen you to be a people,
For his own possession, out of all the people,
That are on the face of the earth.
— Deuteronomy 7:6

Of course, they thought we were the chosen, the exceptional. In the sermon, it was clear that Israel (this part of Wisconsin) had been separated from the nations (the rest of the world). Therefore, we are not to adopt other cultural ways. God chose us. This election was an act of grace that should evoke consecrated service rather than the proud feeling of being God's favorite. Chosen and proud; humble and dependent; wonderful ideas altogether, but as people looked in my direction, I wondered if the notion of exceptionality would be expansive enough to include or exclude me. When you're fourteen, you worry about such things.

To be a Lutheran, I would need to be confirmed. I was already a year or so beyond my confirmation age, but I would still have to take confirmation lessons for a year. This year's class had already started, but I could still join. After confirmation classes ended in April, I would have to pass a test in front of the congregation, and then be confirmed in May. By that time, I would be two years older and a foot taller than all the other confirmands.

Lessons would be on Wednesday nights, and I would enjoy them immensely, but it made for an interesting problem—with football and basketball practice after school, and farm chores after practice, it would be hard to get back into town, unless I drove in myself. I had been driving the tractor and pick-up truck all summer and fall; I'll see what I can talk Happy into tomorrow morning.

23

MONDAY'S FOOTBALL PRACTICE WAS particularly hard. The residue from my poor performance last week was very much present in my mind, as well as in Coach's attitude. I was emotionally exhausted before practice started and even more so after. I was both emotionally and physically beat. The only bright spot was that my confirmation lessons would not start again until next Wednesday.

After chores, one of Happy's nephews drove up the driveway in his 37 Ford coupe, complete with rumble seat. As we walked slowly toward the house, Elmer, the son of Happy's older brother, Raymond, got out of the car and walked toward us. He was about 27 or 28, a Korean War vet, and one rough-looking character. He was short, but with a powerful upper body that seemed too big for his legs.

"Hello," he said. Unshaven, dressed in his army fatigues.

"Elmer, how the hell are you?"

"This is your cousin, Mike." I reached out to shake his hand.

"Mike... Hi, kid. Wanna go shinin' deer tonight?" like he had known me forever.

"We have to get some dinner," Happy said.

"Fine, I'll eat with ya. Then we'll go."

"I am not goin'... You guys go," Happy declared.

As we continued toward the house, the car door opened and out stepped a lovely woman, maybe 20 years old. I had not noticed her until then. She was wearing a beautiful smile, very tight black pants, a white tee shirt, and black gym shoes. To this young teenager, her body looked almost perfect, and approaching us, she looked more like an apparition than a real person. Maybe it was because she seemed so out of place in the driveway of this little farm that was accented by the odor of the barnyard. She belonged on the sidewalks of Chicago and all of a sudden, my mind was taken back to the city. This is what a woman looks like, I thought.

"This is my new wife, Sally," Elmer said.

Happy and I stood in shock, and I 'm not sure if it was the timing of the announcement or simply the question being begged: How did she and he ever get together?

"We were married last month in California and drove here in the Ford."

"Hi, I'm Sally," extending her hand first to Happy and then to me. There was something thrilling in her touch, something beyond my understanding at the time. We all followed Happy into the house, where we both seemed extra-helpful in getting dinner on the table. We had put a chicken in the oven before chores; I came back to the house forty minutes later to complete the roasting bird with some potatoes and carrots. Happy set the table as I served the meal, taking the chicken and vegetables from the roasting pan to a serving dish. The chicken looked and smelled wonderful; I'm sure Sally had something to do with the enhanced atmosphere. There was plenty to go around although it seemed like Elmer ate half the chicken himself.

"Well, you guys ready to go shinin'?"

"You three go. I'm going to clean up the kitchen and go to bed," Happy said again.

Approaching the car, Elmer asked if I wanted to ride in the rumble seat. Without hesitation, I said of course and away the three of us went. Sally and Elmer sat up front, while I took my place in the back.

You can only get into a rumble seat by climbing over the opened rear door that is like a car's trunk door, only it opens from the top down, not up as a trunk would. The space was much larger than I imagined. The seat was leather and there was also room for luggage. In fact, I noticed four boxes and a suitcase sharing the space with me; three people could ride comfortably back here. There was enough room in front of the seat that you can also stand up and look out over the roof of the car.

The Ford was also equipped with a spotlight, the kind a police car might have, and a V-8 engine that gave the car the feel of a racing vehicle. We drove out the driveway onto the road, kicking up gravel dust so thick it insulted the plants along the roadside and interfered with the darkening shades of evening.

After about four miles, Elmer found a cow pasture where he believed deer would be grazing before retiring back into the forest. To me, this didn't seem like a good place to be driving a nice car. But no matter, he turned off the headlights and drove across a shallow ditch that had a culvert with dirt covering it.

The stars were bright enough for us to see a gate; Elmer stopped, opened it, and we were in the pasture. He closed the gate and got back in the car. At this time of year, the cows were no longer out at night, but deer hold no deference for the rules of farmers or the behaviors of cows. They also love pastureland as much as cows do so we started to slowly drive into the night field filled with large boulders, dark holes our eyes couldn't penetrate, and some raspberry bushes.

Elmer turned on the spotlight and about 50 yards ahead in the distance we spot some deer at the edge of the pasture, right where it meets the woods. I wasn't sure why we wanted to do this, but as two deer turned and made a dash across the pasture, Elmer began to chase them. Before I know it, we're traveling maybe twenty miles an hour in hot pursuit. I now stood on the rumble seat and over the roof of the car, I have a clear view of the chase—white tails flying through the night with a light bouncing on and off of them in time with the bumps we encountered over the pasture. It was fun.

Elmer stopped the car and told us we would do one more search and chase. And, Sally, noticing the fun I had in the rumble seat, climbed in with me as Elmer turned off the spotlight and slowly moved to the other end of the pasture. We drove about a quarter of a mile before noticing more deer. At first, they seemed to ignore us. Then Elmer turned on the spotlight again, but they just stood there, blinded by the light.

Then we were off to the races again. Both Sally and I stood to look over the roof of the car and she hung on more tightly with each new bounce. In my young mind, the clinging seemed erotic and I sensed or wanted to believe she was flirting with me. Then she put both her arms around me and kissed my neck. This was very strange. I felt embarrassed and aroused at the same time. I wished that Elmer would stop the car and take us home.

It was almost ten when he decided to leave the pasture and by then, it was getting too cold to ride in the back so all three of us got into the front seat, Sally in the middle.

Except for the starlight which casts earth objects in long shadows, the farm and house are in dappled darkness. No light from within. Happy must be asleep. As I got out of the car, there seemed to be an extra-long goodbye as though Sally and Elmer didn't want to go or maybe had nowhere to go.

One thing I didn't want right then was Sally or Elmer coming into the house. I knew nothing about them. It was all I could do to keep up with myself and Happy, and the thought of others living here was unthinkable.

"I'd better get in. Thanks for the deer shinning; it was fun. "Hope to see you guys soon. Good night," I said, and not looking back, I opened the back door and disappeared inside. What a night. I didn't feel good about it. I should have offered them the opportunity to stay.

It took me longer than usual to wash my hands and face. The feel and scent of Sally seemed to ignore the soap and water and wafted into the night. In my bed that night, I had all kinds of thoughts about Sally and about girls in general.

24

ON THIS PARTICULAR TUESDAY AFTERNOON, football practice went well. It was as though Coach had no recollection of yesterday, and I sure wasn't going to remind him of it with more bonehead plays. We would have our first real scrimmage, and I thought that I could just lie low and watch the action from the sidelines. That didn't happen.

"Hartoonian, get out here and see what you can do at safety," Coach called from the middle of the field. He was going to let me play on the first-string defense? At safety? This was either a mistake or one big joke! Why was he doing this? There wasn't much time for thought. Maybe I had a good head for recognizing plays as they developed, but I 'm only a freshman and I have been playing scared. And, now, I'm scared shitless.

For a moment, I thought about running for the gym and getting out of there! I'm not even sure why I ever went out for this sport in the first place. Baseball and basketball were my loves, but a few other freshmen, particularly Keith had, so I did too. Monkey see, monkey do. Great reason. I was weak in the knees and hoped that Coach was kidding and would tell me to get the hell off the field, before I coughed up my cookies. As I ran out onto the field, my mind raced—I can learn this; I can get over this fear. I knew that while I could play with fear of Coach, of getting hurt, or of just screwing up, I would much rather play for the love of it, the joy or thrill of it. The question was—is there any way that I could rid myself of this overwhelming fear and enjoy the situation I'm in?

I tried to look as confident as the other players, and as I felt the grass under by cleats, I started thinking that maybe this would be my chance to start to like or even love this game. Why not?

Love is within us, built from the many encounters we experience with people and places. Over the years, I have learned that love is like an out-of- body experience. It's a universal value. It is beyond self, but you've got to get your head right. Right-headedness—might be measurable, but love isn't. To the degree that you try to measure love, to that same degree you belittle it. Trying to measure love is destructive. But love is as real as the sun and rain. And it changes you.

The Bible teaches us that God so loved the world that He gave His Only Son to die for us. That love can only be understood symbolically. Elizabeth Barrett Browning in her 43rd sonnet could only answer the question How do I love thee? by counting the ways that are truly unmeasurable, to the depth and breadth and height my soul can reach.

Love, as practiced, is kindness and care. Love as a cultural presentation can only be approached metaphorically through parable, poetry, music, and other symbolic representations.

There is no way that you can be forced to love. You may "learn" to love, but only if it's in you. Love, therefore, cannot be pictured, categorized, or generalized, no matter how hard the advertising world tries to suggest that there is only one way to express love and it's "this way."

Signs and actions of love are driven by our beliefs, and these beliefs come from the ways in which our minds have interacted with the world. These interactions have created perceptions, and our behavior is directed by these perceptions, which we see as descriptive, logical, and true.

Can I love football? Perhaps not, but I can respect these players and the practice or craft of football.

I think I know that love is developed and strengthened by affirming the positive. It's not that love stops all criticism—in fact, it should encourage growth through the loving critiques of behavior.

Do I have any love in me for football? Can I express it on this field? I love athletics in general. That may be a start, but there seems to be only a part of me that has a glimpse of what love is. Perhaps my problem was never having someone or something to love, and more importantly, believing that I never had anyone who really loved me.

Children become good when they know that they are loved, and, they become even better, when they learn how to love. The lucky ones among us learn this early; others of us never do. What do I love? Mark, of course. I love his face. It's just good to be in the world with him. Mama, well yes, but it's a colder relation-ship. I could make a list of people and things, but I'm not really sure that love exists in my life; at least, not the kind of love that makes me feel protected. Now there's a feeling of emptiness to accompany my fear. If I bleed, I will need to stop the bleeding. If

I hurt, I will need to do the comforting. If I learn, I will have to teach myself. I will have to find love within and create the best from what I have. Sounds okay, but I still feel alone. That's not a bad thing, it's just the way it is right now.

A feeling of aloneness and being lonely are not the same thing. You can be alone and not be lonely. I first tell myself that I need motivation—from Coach, from Happy, from who knows what. But that's not right. If I go down the motivation path, I will become needy. Even as a fourteen-year-old, I knew that.

Motivation doesn't work, at least not for long. I believe that it actually corrupts; it's additive and expensive, and you have to keep increasing the dosages. It's better to bypass motivation and go right to identity and purpose. This is simple and straightforward to me. You do things in the best way you can. You approach or work toward excellence because that's who you are. For example, a father does not have to be motivated to care for his family. By virtue of being a father, with attending rights and obligations, a man will do what needs to be done, because purpose and behavior follow from identity. No one needs to motivate him. Playing baseball is not hard if you're a baseball player. No one needs to motivate you, because that's who you are.

I realize that people go around selling motivation, but what they are really selling is corruption and mediocrity. If I am to do anything good on this field, I have to do it because of my identity, my reputation, my character; there is purpose in that, and the love will emerge. This I believe. With these thoughts spinning in my mind, I run out onto the field.

I'm out here. Now what?

"The offense will run three plays. What I want you to do, Hartoonian, is call out as soon as you think you know what's coming. Yell, PASS, or RUN, or UP THE GUT, or REVERSE— whatever you see. Call it, and we'll see. Think you can do that, kid?"

"Yes, sir," I say, not really knowing what he was talking about.

From reading our playbook, it seemed to me that the best way to know what play is coming is to read the uncovered offensive linemen—the ones, or the one, with no one in front of him. If he charges ahead, it's a run. If he steps back with his arms at his chest, it's a pass. If he pulls back and runs to his right or left, the play will go in that same direction. I'll watch the linemen and also keep an eye on the tailback or quarterback. Learn his habits or tendencies. Does he like going to his right 70 percent of the time? And I also need to understand the recent history of the team—are they a running team? A passing team? Conservative or risk-takers?

All this theory is fine, but I 'm starting with no skill and less knowledge...no experience. How can you do well in a situation that discounts your ignorance and fear? But strangely it felt okay out there. I was exposed, but I saw the defense and the whole offense in front of me. Seeing is the second step—after figuring out what's important enough to look at.

The first play was a tailback pass. He started by running to his right. I saw that the left guard had backed into a passing stance. Got to be pass, I thought, and yelled, "PASS!" On a short delay, the left end is running a long crossing pattern, trying to get behind me. I stay with him until he faked what I think is a buttonhook, stopping, and looking back at the tailback, getting me to go for his fake, which I do, and he gained about five yards on me; enough room for a good pass to result in a touchdown.

I tried to catch up to him, but the ball was now in the air. "Shit," I said. But to my surprise, the ball came out short. As the end streaked down the field, I think there is no way this ball is going to catch up to him. As it turned out, the ball was perfectly thrown to ME. All I had to do is catch it and I'll have an interception.

Instinctively, I grabbed the ball, tucked it under my left arm, and thought about running. BAM! I didn't see it coming. Someone hit me so hard I think I broke my leg. Falling to the ground, I dropped the ball, and what should have been an interception was just an incomplete pass.

Smiling, Coach said, "Hit you in a bad place, Hartoonian. Your hands."

The offense ran two more plays, and then three more; and three more after that. The only action I had was to jump on the tailback once, after he was tackled by several teammates, After a while of this, I felt like I needed to do something, which, of course, I didn't. Playing safety isn't so bad, and I felt pretty good when we came off the field for a water break. Maybe I can play after all. My fear was dissipating and I started to sense some feelings of purpose, and perhaps a little accomplishment, no matter how small or insignificant.

We ended practice, as always, with wind sprints and a little pep talk/lecture from Coach. "Tomorrow will be a heavy workday. We'll focus on offense, but we'll also do more fundamentals:

blocking, tackling, and running. Thursday we'll go over our game plans for Friday night. I haven't picked the offensive or defensive teams yet, but you'll all play on Friday, so get your heads in the right place."

25

CLASSES SEEM A BLUR TODAY—MY head is into practice. I really like being in class, any class. Sometimes you learn; sometimes you don't, but in every class, you get to see others and often talk about things that we just don't speak of outside the classroom.

Today, Coach Norman, in civics class, got us talking about the Korean War and the Cold War, and our responsibility to military service. The boys will all have to register for the draft on or before our 18th birthday, and most of us will be drafted or enlist, work on the family farm or the lumber mill, and the few lucky among us will go to college. With the exceptions of the military and mill, the girls were in the same situation, only with fewer options.

"What's your take on the draft? Should everyone serve in the military—men and women?" Coach Norman asked.

The thought never occurred to me before, but I believe that having women drafted would be like having them play football. That's not right. But there are other things they could do for the team. But then again, football may be a poor metaphor. After some discussion, I don't know what to think anymore. That didn't stop me from opening my big mouth though.

"Maybe all of us should be drafted. After all, it can be a good deal: training, food, travel, adventure. More than we have here." I said quietly.

"Yeah, and you can also get killed," Ben said.

"Like people do on the highways, in the mill, deer hunting, and on their farms," Karen rebuffed.

"That's different." Ben wanted to say more, but now everyone was chiming in and Coach told us to respect each other's comments, and quiet down. Then he went on.

"Going into service or being part of any draft may not be about you, but about your country. Wouldn't a draft, where everyone serves, make it our military, not theirs? Shouldn't the army belong to us, not them? Isn't it about being a real part of your nation's history? If you never serve your country, will you regret it? Wouldn't it be fair for all eighteen-year-olds, men and women, to be drafted, to serve in the military or work for the federal government, for example, in an organization like the old CCC camps of the Depression?"

"What's CCC?" Tom asked.

"The Civilian Conservation Corps (CCC) was a public work relief program that operated from 1933 to 1942 in the United States for unemployed, unmarried men from relief families. It was part of the New Deal. You will study about the Great Depression and the New Deal in US History when you are juniors. It was a plan to put young men to work at a time when almost half of the men between the ages of 18 and 25 were unemployed. They worked in the national forests, doing all kinds of things, from planting trees to building roads and bridges through our forests. They were paid a small monthly wage; most of it was sent back to their parents. They lived in barracks, ate in mess halls, and went to classes to learn a skill, and in many cases, to learn how to read and write. In many ways, it was like the military, without the war."

At that moment, the bell sounded and Coach dismissed us with, "Tom, check the library and tell us more about the CCC tomorrow. Then tell us if you think it would work for us today."

My mind was not on tomorrow, but this afternoon.

Football practice was upon me before I knew it. The locker room was quiet as we dressed for the "hard" practice this afternoon. Most of the starting positions were filled; we all knew that despite what Coach said yesterday. But some spots were open and maybe one of the "new guys" would round out the team.

After four 50-yard wind sprints, Coach set the offense. Since we were expected to play both ways, the people playing offense would also play defense; that is, most of them would.

Working with the offensive line first, Coach told Keith to get in at left tackle. Wow, I think, he's letting a freshman start. He called the backfield next, "Roger-tailback, Ron-quarterback, Steve-fullback, and at right halfback ...I think everyone was expecting Joe, another senior, but what do we hear... "Hartoonian, get at right half."

Joe was angry, very angry. A little freshman has moved ahead of him on the depth chart. This would be the start of a serious rivalry between us that lasted through the basketball and baseball seasons and beyond.

Practice went well for me. Nothing special, but I didn't screw up either. Trying to play within your abilities is very important, particularly for a freshman. I can't wait for Friday night. It will be a game I will play in, and a dance after that to look forward to even without a date. Freshmen boys can at least stand around and look interested, if not interesting. Life was pretty good right now.

I told Happy about practice and I thought he was proud of me. He said something to Kurt, who stopped by today, but I hoped not for a long visit.

"Mike's playing Friday. Want to catch the game?" He would try, but both Happy and Kurt would spend Friday night and Saturday morning at the Dew Drop Inn. Both will miss the game and most of Saturday as well. The Saturday morning chores, and more, would be on me.

Right then, though, the cool of late September was a perfect fit for my happy feelings about football, and for the fading, but still-warm sunlight that shone among the gold and red leaves of the sugar maples and poplar trees. The bright, dark greens of the northern pines were now more dominant as they signaled the day of their total reign over the forest. But for now, the color of autumn was breathtaking, and I could think of nowhere else I would rather be. I love the fall—always have, always will.

The months of September and October are precious. They always signify a beginning ... school ... football ... romance. Spring may be the time of earth's renewal, but my season is fall. Wisconsin has done it to me, of the four seasons here, fall is the most beautiful, delicate, and fleeting—like love and life. While spring holds the promise of summer, fall must rely on itself. I like this self-reliance. It fits me. I know that I could get many arguments on the topic of "best" season, but that's in our subjective nature, seeing only that which we believe.

For some days now the autumn sun has warmed my heart,
While the colors of fall play upon my mind,
Like a bittersweet melody.
I laughed sometimes and cried once or twice,
Talked with the trees and some impatient geese,
And played football with boys in a schoolyard.
I prayed too, for your presence,
For I need your love most on days like these,
When the beauty of nature bespeaks the approach of winter.

26

5:30 Friday night. Our first home game. I slipped out of the barn early and told Happy I'd see him after the game. Keith and Lee picked me up and I rode to town with anxiety in and all around me. I saw the same in Keith.

There was a cool breeze in my face, and looking out of the open car window, my mind was filled with football diagrams and Coach's voice yelling and reminding me of all the dumb things I did in practice. But this would be our first game and I could put the past to rest.

This is one of the fundamental mistakes I made then and continue to make still. The past is never at rest. It lives through us, defines us, and sets up illusions and tensions within our minds that often border on folly. If there was one thing I could make any child understand, it would be to think carefully about the present—what you do today and what you say— because today's acts will be with you always, good or bad.

We all make mistakes, and those mistakes will have negative impacts on the present and future only if we can turn the shame of mistakes into guilt. You will hide or lie about shameful acts. You will keep secrets that will impede your growth as a moral being. Guilt, on the other hand, is something you can confess to yourself and others, and perhaps, God. Expose whatever negative things you do or say, so you can give yourself the opportunity for living a better, more honest, life. Forgiveness isn't everything; it's the only thing. The future depends on it.

Keith was starting too, so we could feel sick together.

"This is great. You two freshmen starting tonight. How are you feeling?' Lee asked.

Neither Keith nor I said a word. I felt like I was going to throw up. Keith looked so pale and motionless, I wondered if he was still alive.

In total silence, we both suit up. The locker room is a sea of voiceless activity: ankles being taped, pads being adjusted, trying on the same old stinky helmets, and finally the new uniforms. The manager gives me number 31 and with Keith's help, I proudly pull it over my shoulder pads. I do the same for him, number 55.

I try to sit still but find myself walking around the locker room and into the toilet, where I throw up in the urinal and some splashes on my shoes. As I return, feeling pounds lighter and more at ease, Coach tells us to sit on the chairs in front of the chalkboard or on the floor. At the board, he starts our pre-game lecture.

"This is our first game; it is their first game too. Tonight, we'll find out about ourselves. Understand, however, that their school is twice as large as ours, and they're experienced and BIG! We have some better athletes and we have the home field advantage. And, this is a non-conference game, so we are playing to learn something about ourselves and about having some fun. Enjoyment—that's the way it is for me, and I hope for you. There is nothing more important in high school than to find out something about you—about yourself. We play tonight to find out if we have the heart and mind to compete in this game, as well as in the game of life."

"How you behave here is a good indication of how you will behave in life. Quit on yourself tonight and you'll quit on yourself, and others, tomorrow. I have been hard on you, but you are in the best shape of your life. I have given you a lot to think about, but football, as with all sports, is about your ability to think. Real athletes, regardless of their grades in school, are among the brightest people in any community; you can't play ball well and be stupid at the same time. You may end up uneducated and ignorant about much of life, but you must be a thinker and decision-maker or you are no athlete." Coach went on. "Technically, you are ready for your first game. You all have some knowledge. The starting offense and defense are posted, although, I plan to play most, if not all, of you. Play up to your ability, but stay within your limits of knowledge and your skill of the game. Know what you can do and what you can't, but learn. That's all I ask of you. But it doesn't matter what I ask of you, it's what you ask of yourself and your teammates…that's what really counts."

I liked what Coach was saying, but understood or heard only some of it. I was just too nervous. I saw that I was starting at right-half and second on the depth chart at safety on defense. I ran back to the toilet and try to throw up again.

Running out of the locker room onto the field was emotionally overwhelming for me. The cheerleaders formed two lines for us to run through, and the clear, early evening was breathtaking, perhaps because I had trouble breathing.

From that moment, fall and football would be linked in my mind. The sights, sounds, and smells of the game are buried deep within my consciousness, recallable at the drop of a thought. The combination of evening air filled with the smells of harvest, sweat, grass smears, popcorn, and fear, can still over-power my senses.

We won the coin toss and would receive. I wasn't on the kick-off return team so watched from the side, trembling so hard that I wondered if my legs would carry me into the huddle.

Once I got on the field, my feelings changed and my fear subsided a little. I was loving being out there and that was erasing my fear. Love always beats fear. More focused now, I reached the huddle as Ron started to call the first play. Coach would give the quarterback three plays to call and run in sequence, regardless of success or lack thereof. If we were successful after three plays and still on offense, he would then send plays in by alternating right guards, sending in a play with a different guard each time. If we failed to get a first down in the first three plays, we would punt. We punted, and I returned to the sideline to watch our defense and listen, with apprehension, for my name coming from Coach's angry lips.

"What the hell are you guys doing out there? Hartoonian, you're supposed to block out there, not stand around with your head up your ass. Hit something, for Christ's sake."

Before he could continue, our opponent scored, and with less than three minutes played, we found ourselves behind seven to nothing. After they kicked off again, we attempted two running plays to the right and gained one yard. A new right guard came running onto the field with a third-down play.

On third and nine, Coach called for a pass … to me. The flow of the play was to the right again, but this time, the tailback would stop as he approached the right end and throw a pass to me. My job was to fake a block, keep my feet, work my way through the line, and run a post pattern toward the middle of the field, trying to get behind the safety. As the ball came toward me, I realized that I couldn't beat the safety, and besides, the ball was thrown short. I adjusted by breaking in front of the safety, making contact, but both of us were able to keep our feet. The ball seemed to hang and allowed two more of their defensive backs to cover me. I focused on the ball and jumped as high as I could.

From among the three defenders, I surprised myself by coming down with the ball on their forty-yard line. As I hit the ground, with the ball still in my possession, all three of them hit me and one of them came down hard on my left foot, breaking my big toe. Welcome to Wisconsin high school football. We made the first down, but lost the game 28, zip. The doctor, on the sidelines, said that there was little to be done for a broken toe but immobilize it some. "Go home, take some aspirin, and sleep." No dancing for me tonight.

When Keith and Lee dropped me off at 10:30, I went up to bed. Happy wasn't home. I tried to pay little attention to the empty house. Besides, the broken toe overwhelmed my senses. Something seemed wrong, however. I heard the cows. They shouldn't be making noise at this time of night and then it occurred to me that they hadn't been milked yet. I changed my clothes, went back downstairs, and hobbled out to the barn. As the barn door opened, the cows seem crazy. They are trying to tell me something in the loudest way. They were hungry and hurting from holding their milk.

I hobbled over to the feedbox, about ten feet long by four feet wide and three feet high in size, and filled a cart with powdered oats, corn, and an array of vitamins and minerals. I gave each cow about a quart so they would quiet down and I could begin to milk them. I would feed them hay after finishing.

The milking machines were in the milk house and I struggled to use all three of them, but gave up and decided to go with just two. As I brought the machines into the barn, it occurred to me that before I started to milk, the barn would have to be cleaned. The shit from all day had to go, and new bedding and lime had to be spread.

Cleaning the barn takes me a good half hour and now at 11:15, I started the milking. Funny, I don't feel the least bit tired now and my toe actually feels better than it did when I got home. I do feel alone and angry. At midnight, at the age of fourteen, with a broken toe and restless cows, it's like God has gone up to Heaven to sleep and left me here alone to feel and think.

27

Again, there is that sense of being alone that's different from being lonely. Doing these chores at midnight certainly generate sadness or a feeling of being victimized. But I didn't feel put upon, or in any way, sad. I'm a little pissed at Happy simply because I would like to live with a sense of fairness and being able to count on someone, but right now, the sense of accomplishment I feel overcomes the feelings of being treated unfairly. And besides, milking the cows this evening felt good, broken toe and all. Perhaps, happiness is something not deserved, but something earned—earned by working and accomplishing something, like catching a football that seemed impossible to catch and milking these cows alone. I'm realizing that happiness is a result of trying to accomplish something good or useful.

I'm beginning to see the tension between the child and the adult within me—between dependency and independency. Losing a football game, breaking a toe, and milking cows, may seem more like disappointments or punishment than accomplishments for a child, but I was seeing these as adult accomplishments. Child or adult, I guess you never deserve to be happy; it simply happens when you feel it is earned through moving beyond whatever pain and engaging your responsibility.

Walking dejectedly back to the house and up to my bedroom to change my shirt and put on some clean pants. I really do feel good. Didn't expect that. I was alone, and I didn't know enough about tomorrow to be concerned with the necessities of life. I wasn't even sure if there was enough food for breakfast, or if Happy would be home for morning chores. But tomorrow is Saturday, and right now, I'm content. This farm was becoming a real place in my life. I live here, I was contributing to it, and I was making memories and connecting them to the people. That makes a difference in life. I was beginning to care.

A farm, or a house, or even a town changes if someone you know, or care for, lives there, and when you give or accomplish something for that town or person. Often, when driving through the countryside, I pick out a house and consider how my life's work would be different had I grown up there or fallen in love with the person who lived in this or that place.

If you happen to love someone who lives in a particular house, then that house takes on a special characteristic. But it's the person! It's always the person. Without loved and loving people, things and places are quickly drained of meaning. I was beginning to understand.

A house can be full of people, but you can still come home to an empty place. A city can be exciting, crowded, and full of life, and still be empty. The comfort feeling will not appear without love. And, perhaps, love will not appear without contributing. It takes work to build love.

Intimacy has as many possible places as there are occasions for humans to truly connect. Intimacy between people does not demand knowing a great deal about each other's life; it simply grows from a mutual awareness and the excitement of sharing thoughts and activities. Pessimistic thoughts can also be accepted when they appear from a base of love. However, intimacy is only enriched through positive thoughts. Mutually affirming thoughts grow happiness, and the wise know that love is better when spiced with a sprinkle of sadness and fear. This is the covert truth and the dilemma faced by those interested in love—the only way to have or be in love is to create a place of love, yet the only way to create a loving place is to have or be in love. This dilemma causes us to make special places—places where memories are made and places where a house is turned into a home. What is nice to know is that we can create places of intimacy; I can do this.

Places of intimacy cannot be planned nor captured because they spring from that unexpected human exchange that fuses the physical and intellectual with the spiritual. These places are elusive, yet personal, and they entreat memory, as opposed to history; chance as opposed to will; and grace as opposed to duty.

Certainly, we can get to history, will, and duty through intimacy, but we can't get to intimacy through history, will, or duty. Intimacy is different. It involves the transcendence of ordinary objects, noble work, and human-made beauty, to an embrace of our deeper selves—an independent presence. That's how I felt, after midnight, that early Saturday morning, an independent presence, and maybe for the first time.

1:00 a.m. I pour myself a bowl of Wheaties, sit at the kitchen table and begin to read some stories in the monthly dairy journal that Happy has been receiving for years. Mama threw out hundreds of copies when we moved in. In this very early morning, I was able to only look at pictures of cows and grains, and headlines about research in milk production and artificial insemination.

My toe started to hurt again. Sitting was making it worse. I closed the journal, finished my cereal, and walked up to my bedroom. I turned out the lights and sat up in bed as my mind had no interest in sleeping. I thought again about relationships and place, now with a focus on place.

How do I assemble a place of intimacy?

Place can, indeed, hold us at its mercy. Home, however, transcends all. Home, by definition, is a profound place, and for good reason. It's not only the people or things; it's the enchantments of memory, both happy and sad. Our memories of places and people can both cheer us and tear us apart.

The smell of baking bread, the voice of a lover, the sound of softly falling rain—all add up to make a house a home. It's an accumulative, and not a reductionist, phenomenon; the rain, lover's voice, and bread are full of meaning today because of events gone by but secure in memory.

I was content now thinking about the possibility of making a home here, and sleep came.

The morning arrived far too soon. I heard Happy and Kurt downstairs and I hobbled down in more pain than I had last night.

"You guys going to the barn?" I asked, adding, "I broke my toe in the game last night."

"Did you win, or is your team too nice to beat another?"

"Too nice?" I said in a questioning voice. I wondered if Happy would ask about the milking last night, but he didn't. I wondered if he would ask about how I got hurt, but he didn't. As with a great many things in life, I didn't understand Happy; I just had to get used to him. Perhaps I would understand some-day, but the situation was strange, like being dropped into a culture. Sometimes they must think I'm a potted plant. Turning this place into a home would be harder than I thought. Maybe impossible, because this house and region rested on a disappearing culture.

People here seem to believe that outsiders will never make a home in this place. They think that this is the way it was and will forever be. They don't understand that the family farm and their attending life style is dying; that most of these farm kids I play ball with will live in cities; that the world is going big-time global; and, they will not be able to hold their children in this cultural place and time. Without attention to these changes, their homes will soon be gone.

Looking back, I think I knew that the farm would never hold me. It would never be my home. I might sympathize with the farmers here, but they can't force me or force their own children to stay put in the name of some cultural harvest that is fast drying up and blowing away. As families or as a society, we cannot afford to subsidize a way of life that is archaic. Enabling isolationists to practice their ideological hunches while, at the same time, dismissing reasoned thought, makes no cultural or economic sense. All this does is encourage behavior that is dysfunctional to a dynamic, democratic society. This traditional and fundamentalist attitude toward culture, which is based almost entirely on fear of a changing world, will never succeed or help the next generation, because it gets in the way of making use of the necessary knowledge available to us. In fact, it denies reason, replacing it with that style or faith that is blind and dumb.

What to keep? What to throw away? What to build anew? We never asked these questions. And, our government's policies worked against us.

In the early 1950s, almost forty percent of our nation's people engaged in some aspect of agriculture. Seventy years later, less than two percent of Americans are thus engaged, but still produce over thirty times more food and fiber. No matter how hard the people in and around New Kassel would try to hold onto their farms, and their beliefs, they were already disappearing.

People who want to hold only to the old ways, as good as they might have been or not, are not just holding to some sense of authenticity of food, language, habits, relationships, and worship; they're holding on to what is already dying. We have a need to control our world, but at the same time, we know we can't, so we freeze the past, and bring it forward. It's an illusion, and a harmful one. Again, every community must decide what to throw away, what to keep, and what to build anew. These activities render out the good of society and pass it on to the next generation. But this can only happen if people understand that they have a generational covenant with the past and the future.

Happy and many of the people who hold fast to defending this island of stagnation were not champions of the past. They did not know the difference between insular and sophisticated behavior.

In a global world, where markets and political thoughts are discussed and applied, only a cosmopolite or one who understands the synergy of E Pluribus Unum can live, and not just survive; only a cosmopolite can be a citizen and not just a subject. Happy, like Uncle Vartin before him, were both insular and subjects, all their sincerity of ethnicity notwithstanding. In their own ways, they were irrelevant to our republic, because they refused to judiciously engage in change.

The ethnic serves a wonderful democratic purpose, but only in continual debate with the ideas of the cosmopolite. The real and continuing cultural debate seeks to address the contradictions inherent in the values of diversity and unity which define our republic.

To achieve unity, what elements of history, language, and philosophy do we need to hold in common? To achieve diversity, what attending rights and responsibilities do we have to our families and communities, to our ethnicities and our nation?

At about 6:15; Happy and Kurt leave for the barn and I walk out after them just to see if the hangover duo could milk a cow. I throw feed into the mangers and tell the two of them that I will make breakfast.

It was a beautiful morning and toe notwithstanding, we would spend most of it, as well as the many days ahead, getting the last of the corn off the field, shucking it, and putting the cobs in the corncrib. At this time of year, we had to make the most of every good day. I hoped that Kurt would hang around and help.

28

"FOLLOW THE EMOTION YOU'RE HAVING. Your gut is right," Uncle used to say. On this first day of November, I was struggling with my emotions. I could feel them, but I couldn't describe them. My mind was scattered. Basketball practice starts later this week and I still hobbled from a serious lack of conditioning, dating from the broken toe.

Because my football season ended the way it did, I'm not in shape to run the basketball floor. The only plan I have is to run home after school today on Tuesday and again on Wednesday, and also jump rope each day, so I will have legs on Thursday when practice starts. It's only three and a half miles, and if the weather holds and we don't get a lot of snow, it should help my conditioning. I can also do fifty push-ups and jumping-jacks each day when I get home. That was my plan; now to follow through.

Classes were going well, Happy has been home for chores, at least most of the time, and Mama, and perhaps, Mark would be home for Thanksgiving. This is all good. Our first game is on the Tuesday before Thanksgiving, and I wanted to start on the freshman or junior varsity team. I have about one week to prove myself.

At a few minutes after three, I run down to the locker room to put on my Converse high-tops—white, of course—an old sweatshirt left over from football practice, and a stocking cap. The day was clear and calm, about 33 degrees, and I start my run for home. I will have to figure a way to bring running clothes with me on the bus tomorrow, at least some sweatpants and gloves.

My mind now turns to the road—cold and long. From where the school is located, it takes me about ten minutes to reach the edge of town. Ahead, the road and the countryside beyond are held in that strange tension between fall and winter. The struggle for final control is foreknown, but today, fall is putting up a fight and the result is both beautiful and poignant. Within a week, all this could be under a foot of snow, but today I'm safe.

I'm running too fast. At this pace, I will never make it home without walking, so I slow down a bit, just in time to hear a school bus behind me and kids laughing at the dumb freshman running in the cold. The bus passes with uncomfortable noise and it will no doubt beat me home, but not by much, I hope. Happy won't have time to wonder where I am.

The road first takes me through a swamp where the cattails look brown and frozen and some quail seem to be hiding as I move past. There is such a feeling of closeness with the road. Everything is right there for me to experience. The wild grasses along the side of the road take on a familiarity that makes them my friends and traveling companions.

Up a short hill and into a gentle curve, the road passes through a small woodlot used as a pasture but at this time of year, the stones and boulders dominate, more plentiful than the brown and golden grasses waving in the breeze among them. The road turns south and the afternoon sun, lying close to the horizon, is almost warm upon my face.

In the three miles ahead, I will pass seven farms before turning off the blacktop road, running the last half mile on gravel to our driveway. The cadence of my feet hitting the road, brings peace of mind.

While running, there is time for thinking, time for remembering, and time to plan. That is why I have continued to run most of my life. Running helps me focus on the beautiful as well as the distressed, images of our environment and the afflicted nature of our thoughts. The trick, of course, is to know the difference between joy and sadness without the ad man or the people next door dictating what kind of happiness we should pursue. Running helps me feel more deeply about what is true regarding the happiness and pain of my life.

Yet, even with the ability to make my body and mind perform at high levels, I am without self-reflection. I try. I truly try. My problem is that I have no diversions, or don't know now to identify and use the ones I have. Some claim that diversion is the ordinary remedy for ailments of the soul. They believe that the mind must be diverted to other interests, people, cares, or business.

I believed that I didn't have time for diversions. Besides, in order to work, diversions needed self-reflection. I just focused on my work—farm, athletics, self-care, studies. To me, diversions, like vacations, were nonsense. I conclude that diversions only made sense if you conceive of your life's work as a series of insular tasks and not as a natural, systemic whole. The need for diversion is, perhaps, a symptom of a fragmented life, and a roadblock to identity and meaning. I was without guidance or direction, but confident in my juvenile ignorance...the worst of both worlds. It's true that youth gives way, but to what? I wanted to be a man. And, I knew, only dimly—nevertheless knew—that real maturity meant doing what must or should be done, and knowing as well that there would be a high personal cost to pay. My youth was not being misspent. It seemed to be gone.

Doing what must be done is called courageous behavior. This is what heroes are made of. This is a man. This is a woman. Not a child. Yet, most of the time, like a child, I was afraid. Afraid of ... failing ... who cared? Only me? Perhaps. I'm often ashamed ... of what, I didn't really know, but I hid anyway. I shrank my world. Making my world grow smaller, I held to the disastrous fantasies of small-town greatness. I wanted to live life larger, but I had little perspective—little or no clue of what it took to achieve a more comprehensive view of myself. I was held or touched by few people or things.

Arriving home, it's difficult to account for those three miles and the thirty minutes spent in their company. Somewhere, almost by magic, time and space were lost. The best of time is wasted time as Uncle would have said. Here at home, I did not have the luxury to dwell on that lost time of the last half-hour journey. Time passes, often unaccounted for, but I was immediately accountable for the cows. The run was good in itself. Just being on the road, I lost fear and felt refreshed. Without thought, there is joy through exertion, and that joy I could ride into tomorrow. Doing the run was not that important; being the runner was. That helps me engage in the cheerful burden of my present reality by simply being.

In my years, houses and homes were built, children grew up, friends were made and lost, love came a few times, and work sustained it all. I bought all this with my time. There is really no accounting practice that will settle up with the soul for the passing of time no matter how many accomplishments are accumulated.

We have such weak theories about the "whys" of the present condition that we mostly elect to live in our historical imaginations, re-conceptualizing the past out of self-adoration or fear. We do this at great expense. And, we do this simply because of our human need to remember positively. Positive remembering will not do, however, as it allows us to innocently cover up our regrets, sins, and resentments. These cannot be concealed or destroyed. The brain stores them and every once in a while, our memory, over which we have little control, will expose the fidelity of the past. Without an intentional struggle for a contested and clarifying truth of remembrance, we are only capable of embracing a mundane present.

What is even worst, the future is made problematic when we create a glorious, imaginary past leaving the present again in a state of pale imitation. We could, perhaps should, carry more respect for time gone by and take more time to reflect on it, as well as on times to come. As it is, though, we are left with a sense of personal history, which is always corrupt and inaccurate, and a fantasy future, thus, leaving us with only the perspective of today, which is a contraction in terms.

I still tend to link the past and future, as they join me in the present—a temporal region often made trivial by memories and fears. I have this numbing feeling that I can't create a future, because my future is filled with the debris of yesterday, and fragments of life are poor building materials.

I can taste the air, feel the setting sun, and right now my body, the chores, the food, and the deep rest that comes from knowing that the past and future will be kept at bay in the business of the moment, but no matter how delightful, being busy can never be a replacement for building a life of meaning.

29

THURSDAY AFTERNOON CAME WITH A MIX of feelings. We all dressed for basketball practice in silence. Thirty-one guys are trying out for the teams, and the breakdown of numbers would fall something like twelve for varsity, twelve for JV, and as many freshmen who tried for that team. I guessed freshmen don't get cut; they cut themselves.

Three or four of the junior varsity would suit up with the varsity, and at least six freshmen would suit-up with the JV. Coach Anderson was looking for about twenty, maybe twenty-two players to fill all three teams and about ten will be cut. All the sophomores who are cut can still practice, as can the freshmen. The seniors and juniors who are cut, however, were gone.

The philosophy of coaches varies a lot regarding what to do with upper classmen who don't make the final cut. Anderson was clear—if a sophomore was as good as a senior, the sophomore would stay and the senior would go. He believed that this philosophy would force players to work harder and establish themselves as good players, so when they became upper classmen, they would be able to outshine the freshmen and sophomores. In fact, the philosophy simply worked to make everyone better, unless, of course, you were that rare individual who didn't physically mature until his senior year.

Coach Anderson blew his whistle at 3:45 as the last person, a freshman, entered the gym from the locker room. "Over here," Coach yells, and we all grabbed seats on the bleachers. "I am glad to welcome you to what should be a good season. We have an experienced number of upper classmen returning and I'm looking for one or two sophomores and maybe even a freshman to make this year's team. We may not be the best team in the conference, but we will be the best-conditioned team in the conference, and one of the tallest. We have three people above six-two and some pretty quick individuals as well. If we learn and play up to our ability and play together...I would not enjoy playing against us this year. I will teach you how and why we play this game, but I can't play it for you; that's your job. Learn well and execute better...and...we'll have a season that we can all be proud of. Now let's get started."

I noticed that the team manager picked up all the basketballs and took them to the equipment room. We would not see a ball tonight.

"Line up on the baseline in groups of six...on the whistle, sprint to the foul line, touch it with your hand, come back to the baseline, touch it, sprint to the center line and back again, then to the foul line, and finally to the far baseline and back. As all of us know, except for one or two of you freshmen, this is our energy drill, and it will tell us who is in shape. It will tell you if you have the energy to play for me. The last person to finish in each group well join the next group, and I sure as hell hope that you beat someone, because one of you may be running all night ...you get the idea ... I want you running full out, all the time. Energy, men!"

SCREECH … and the first group is off. I am in the second. On the second whistle, my group takes off and I tell myself that I will not be last. I'll see if my days of running home have improved my conditioning. The energy drill should be my kind of drill. I seem to be quicker than most and my toe feels fine. We went from one running drill to another. Defensive drills, running backwards, jumping rope, and skipping drills—but no basketballs. In fact, an hour and a half go by and still no balls. All of us seem to be having trouble just standing, so we finish practice with ten laps around the gym and walk to the showers.

Day two. Basketballs seemed to cover the floor, inviting us to shoot around. In about five minutes, Coach calls us over to the bench and begins to tell us that he prefers that we shoot our free-throws underhanded. That is, "using two hands, hold the ball on each side, bend your knees, keep your back straight, and follow through as you release the ball, ending with both arms above your head pointing toward the basket." He demonstrated and made three in a row.

In Chicago, I had learned to shoot free throws with the same motion I used to shoot my set shot. I had also learned a bit about the jump shot, which would not come into its own for another year or so. Even though we were supposed to be shooting free-throws his way, I tried to impress Coach by taking what must have been a poor excuse for a jump shot. When I thought he was looking, I took the shot. He saw it.

"What the hell was that, Hartoonian? Knock it off. Your feet must stay on the floor when you shoot."

"Free throws ... FREE throws, that's all I want. Nothing else. You must make ten in a row before you shower tonight. I have a cot in my office for anyone who can't do that."

I liked the jump shot but would shoot the free throw the same as I shot the set shot, with my feet on the floor. Coach didn't seem to mind as long as I made my ten in a row.

That year we would play two schools where a player or two could shoot jump shots and they were teams almost impossible to beat. It was like fighting with muskets when the other army had repeating rifles. Coach noticed that things were changing and allowed us to experiment. Perhaps the biggest change was the fact that this would also be the last year of the "keyhole;" that area in front of the basket up to the free-throw line, including the arch beyond. From above, it did look like a keyhole. Offensive players, particularly big players, could just camp out there on offense and, when given the ball, could score almost at will.

By my sophomore year, the three-second rule would be installed, and the keyhole would be widened to become a rectangle, from the base line to the free-throw line as wide as the existing arch—the same arch above the free throw we had always had. This rule made it a little easier for the six-footer or smaller guy to play around the basket because no giant could stand under the basket for more than three seconds. The big guys had to become more mobile and over time they did, changing the game quite dramatically.

I loved the movement the new rule caused. It changed the game to more perfectly fit my style. It made the game faster and more fun to play because more and more players began to shoot jump shots with increasing accuracy. The changes diminished old team patterns and team work, and provided for more individualism, as well as more trade-offs between unity and diversity—adding a bit more diversity.

This second day of practice ended again with more free throws. We could leave practice as soon as we made ten in a row. If we missed, we had to run the energy drill and start shooting again—from zero. I had to run the drill three times, but on my third try, I made ten without a miss and slowly walked into the locker room, showered, and waited for Keith; his mother would drive us home. I thought that practice went well and so did Keith, but too tired to talk, we sat in silence all the way home.

30

In Coach Norman's Civics class today, we were taught how to "duck and cover" on the chance that the USSR might drop an H-bomb on us. This is nuts, I thought. No one is going to bomb the Wisconsin countryside. We also listened to a recording by Edward Teller, the inventor of the bomb, telling how we should not fear it, but embrace it—the bomb, that is. The message was that we gained control of the world by winning WWII, and the world's economy and its supply of oil was ours for the taking. Now we needed to continue and expand that control through nuclear energy.

Even then, I was sure I didn't want to embrace the bomb. We were testing nuclear bombs in the skies near Las Vegas, and people went there to watch the mushroom clouds. We were afraid of the USSR and Communism because, as Coach said, we didn't know how to attack their ideas or support ours.

Instead, we attacked the loyalty of Americans who saw a different future and the need for different public policies. We wondered how a nation like ours could be beaten by North Korea. Of course, it wasn't North Korea, but the subtle nature of the Cold War with China and the USSR that beat us. No one wanted to start WW III, so we signed a truce, and some say, kept the peace. We were also afraid of Communists in our own country and thought it necessary to prop up unpopular leaders all over the world like the Shah of Iran or Carlos Castillo Armas in Guatemala. We didn't want Communism to spread through-out the world, so we would try to contain it.

Coach went on by saying that if Karl Marx had seen the American Century or how our "Oil Century" and technology had changed the worker and producer in America into consum-ers, he, Marx, would have written something very different.

By the 1950s, we were becoming less concerned with ideas, debates, education, and even with culture.

We were becoming a consumer nation where style was replacing function and substance, and consumption replacing production. We were becoming interested in service industries and production processes. Marx, on the other hand, was all about class warfare and surplus value (profits) that came from the accumulation of capital, and the gulf between super-rich and the poor. His idea was that this struggle would only end in revolution.

We read about a guy speaking in Georgia and Alabama by the name of King who was talking about how Americans were killing each other and denying basic rights to Negros. Coach told us about a boy our age, about fourteen, Emmett Till, who was shot and his body was thrown into the Tallahatchie River in Money, Mississippi for allegedly offending a white woman in her family's grocery store.

All these things made us a little sick, but we also countered Coach with statements about how America was good and fun; we had Marilyn Monroe and Marlon Brando, Milton Berle, the Nelsons, Lucille and Desi, Mickey Mantle on television. We had drive-ins, bigger and bigger cars, and more new highways. I could still listen to baseball on the radio, sometimes even the Brooklyn Dodgers.

Coach suggested that these media pictures were far from the reality of how many Americans lived, and we should look around—even to the Native peoples living next door. These issues, contradictions, and questions, however, continued to come at us in school and from outside as well. But given the boundaries of our adolescent context, we had little under-standing. Therefore, the issues of the day assaulted us—without attracting our attention. It was a time to be frightened, to be excited, and to learn. In the dynamics and confusion of the time, though, adults taught us things that were off the mark—indeed, many were lies.

I get a kick out of people today who refer to the 1950s as some kind of calm, happy, mindless period. Looking back at that time, I know that the fifties were much more a time of war, Cold War, economic recessions, social unrest, racial inequities and tensions, sexual awakenings, family dysfunctions, oppression of women, and the beginnings of deep cultural divides spearhead-ed by attitudes of entitlement, consumption, sexuality, athleti-cisms, and nationalism.

Things have become clearer to me over the years. Perhaps the most important is the notion that there exists an inverse relationship between populist nationalism and functional citizenship. We have mastered the former and have unwittingly, yet systematically, turned the concept of citizenship into a narrow and personal perception of rights. For the most part, the fifties began our slow contemporary evolution into subject-hood. That is, we were governed by myths and fears that could not be shaken by evidence. Evidence, the shield of the democratic citizen, was slowly and freely given away by Americans unwill-ing to take responsibility for their own ignorance. Who needs evidence when the government, the economic powerful, and media tell you what is true and what is fake. Still, we didn't care.

I can't ever remember any of us calling ourselves 'American Citizens' when asked our identity. Our nation was asking less and less of us. The government and big business would play a larger part on our lives. The message was clear: "You go shopping and we'll take care of everything else."

I think about our first revolution with the cry of "no taxation without representation." We don't seem to understand that "representation without taxation" is even worse for a democracy. Democracy is not free. We are clear about the need to separate the church and the state. But it is just as important to understand the ethical synergy that must exist between the market and the government.

Our government tells us that things will be easy—all we need to do is vote and leave the rest to leaders in Washington or Madison. By the 1950s, the number of people voting, however, started to decline.

Coach asks us a question that interrupts my thought pattern. "Why are you in school?" And, again, we can't find a good answer to this question, or to the other questions that adults don't ask of us about relationships with each other and why it's so important to think about the future. Of these and other concerns, our culture is mute, and we, the young, are left bewildered.

It seemed to most of us boys that we had the same three futures that were available to our fathers, the military, the mill, the farm. In a changing world where societal norms were being thrown into the air, these choices made little sense.

31

Practice on Friday afternoon was particularly interesting. Coach picked a "starting five" for the varsity and ran them through offensive rotations and defensive sets against the Jr. Varsity. He chose only upper classmen for the varsity; the rest of us were on the JV. This was just a walk through for the real thing.

I suspected that Coach wanted to see if the juniors and seniors remembered anything from last year. It was clear that one of the sophomores would play varsity; he was better than all but one senior, but for now, Jerry was with us. I got a chance to guard Joe, the senior point guard, and our rivalry continued immediately, as though we were still playing football, which to me seemed not a month, but years ago. I didn't believe I could beat him out of a starting job, but I made up my mind to at least keep up with him.

Coach's philosophy helped. If an underclassman can play as well as a senior, the underclassman starts. I wanted to test that. It was as though Coach felt the rivalry too and wanted to test it. He blew his whistle and asked the team to sit on the bleachers.

"Joe, get out here." He threw the ball to Joe at mid-court. "Mike, see if you can take the ball away."

I walked up to Joe and took a defensive position. He gave me a good fake, got around me, and took the ball to the hole before I realized what happened—a real wake-up call.

"Well, freshman, bring it back and score!"

"Joe, don't let him."

I took the ball and started down the floor. Joe was all over me. As I attempted to move around him, he pushed my hip and I went down, hitting my wrist on the floor. While down, he picked up the ball and threw it at my head. I caught it.

"What's the matter, freshman? Can't play a man's game?"

Coach didn't say a thing. I took the ball again, looked at Joe with all the nastiness a fourteen-year-old could muster and started my dribble. Joe was as tall as I but outweighed me by twenty pounds. He knew how to use his body and I felt his powerful hands on my hips, stomach, and arms.

I begin to move him down the floor, pivoting and faking, using all the moves I knew. I finally got the opening I needed and scored a lay-in.

"Shit," Joe cried out.

He goes again, then me. As the rest looked on, this went on for about ten minutes and both Joe and I are exhausted. But he holds no advantage. I thought that I did okay.

Coach said, "Not bad, not bad at all."

He blew the whistle and motioned everyone on the floor. We all paired up, one on one, and tried our best to defend and score. It didn't take long for all of us to be exhausted.

After about a ten-minute passing drill, the varsity took the floor and moved through their patterns; we follow along, pretending to play defense.

"Move it, defense!" We hear the command and begin to play like we mean it. As in football, the upper classmen were men and we were still boys. They were simply bigger, faster, and stronger than the freshmen, and more, they also seemed to know what they were doing.

The next three weeks of practice were filled with embarrassments, mostly mental mistakes that I had to overcome or I might not even make the JV. All I could do was try to learn as much as I could. I volunteered for every drill, to play every defensive set, and even asked Coach if he had any of the patterns written down so I might study them. He didn't. In spite of the uncertainties at home and the problems of adjusting to my new situations, I enjoyed the week of practicing, and into our second week, I hoped that I might even start on the JVs.

Our first game was the Tuesday night before Thanksgiving. Two weeks away. Deer-hunting season would open the Saturday after Thanksgiving at dawn. Happy asked if I wanted to go hunting that morning. I told him I didn't, but would do chores so he and Kurt could go early.

"I'll go hunting on Sunday," I said.

The work is overwhelming. Not just the barn or field work, but the addition of the house chores, particularly in winter. Keeping the place somewhat clean and the fire burning in the furnace could have been a full-time task, and I felt like no one else cared.

"If you don't get one on Saturday, we can go out together on Sunday," I told him again.

He said, "Sounds like a good plan." That was the end of it.

On the 14th of November, we experienced our first snow-storm of the year that actually turned into a blizzard. It started in the afternoon and by the time milking was finished, we could hardly see our way back to the house. It was a complete whiteout. Anyone still on the road would be in serious trouble. I listened to the wind and the radio for a bit, and then went to bed.

It was early, too early, and I tried to read myself to sleep with my literature text for tomorrow's class, but the wind was so loud and the falling snow became so heavy that I gave up reading to stare at the whiteness outside my bedroom window. All I could see were the small branches of the box elder tree discharging their loads of snow with each new gust of wind. In the hypnotic motions of wind and snow, sleep soon came.

The morning was cold and beautiful. Beyond description. Breathtaking. On the walk back to the house after milking, it became clear that this was no ordinary snowstorm. As first light touched the new snow, the white surface of the earth sparkled in diamond hues of red, gold, white, and cold blue. There were no longer any lines of demarcation between the road and fields, the driveway and lawn, the house and garage.

The cold whiteness covered all indications of human activity, and the only sign of life came from some sparrows sitting on the electric wires that stretched between the house and yard pole. Snow drifts were as high as the roof of the garage and sculpted drifts in all shapes engulfed trees, the machine shed, the milk house, and the fence along the road.

I stood in the cold, stared and marveled. I had never seen anything like this. The temperature was much colder than last night, and the stillness and color of daybreak gave a surreal appearance to the morning. I was freezing, but the beauty was irresistible, so I lingered a bit. Besides, we certainly would not have school today.

At about 7:15, I noticed smoke coming from the one-room schoolhouse on the corner.

"Are they having school today?" I asked Happy.

"Sure, the teacher lives with Emma and John and that's only a half mile from the school. The kids all walk; they'll make it in fine."

"Do you think the high school will be open today?"

"School never closes for snow. As soon as the plow comes through, the school bus will follow right behind. And the milk truck will follow the bus; the milk must be picked up before noon or we and the cheese factory lose our asses. The milk truck will get through, so the bus might as well too, 'en so?"

I couldn't believe it, but I thought I'd better clean-up for school just in case Happy was right. Sure enough, at about 7:50, the plow came soaring by, as on wings and almost invisible in the cover of the flying snow coming off its big V-plow. Twenty minutes later, the school bus arrived with many students on board.

There were still several drifts that the plow could not remove from the road, and just before turning onto the main road, we hit one. Our driver stopped, removed a shovel from under his seat, went out and shoved a path through the drift so the bus could proceed. We were all willing to get out and push, but he said, "No!" We arrived at school about an hour late. To this day, I know that dairy farmers will do anything to get their milk to market; a snow event of thirteen inches and thirty-five mile-an-hour winds could not withstand such determination.

On entering math class, it was clear that several kids took the day off. Our attendance was rewarded with a test. We have a substitute teacher today.

"When you finish the problem, just go to the gym. As we have shortened periods today, we are allowing continuous dancing and games all day. My guess is that you will need the whole period to solve the problem anyway. Well, let's get to it."

The math problem was about some guys who want to buy bottles of milk.

Two guys decided to spend their day's wages to buy some milk for their families. Tom was able to buy seven bottles. Don could afford only five.

Just as they were about to purchase the milk, Mark showed up. He asked to join them. He offers to pay $8.40. If all three boys share the milk equally, how much of the $8.40 should Tom receive?

It looks like each share should be 4 bottles. In that case, Tom gives Mark 3 bottles and Don gives Mark 1. If that is true they should split Mark's money in the ratio of 3:1.

Proof: (got to have proof, right?), so I write:

$3x + x = \$8.40$

$x = \$2.10$

Tom gets $3x$ ($6.30) and Don receives x ($2.10)

It seemed right, so I hand it in and head to the gym to wait for the period to end. I see Sharon and Alice dancing and wanted to try it too, but just can't get up the nerve to ask. Ben's playing some new 45s: Elvis Presley's *It's All Right, Mama* and Bill Haley's *Rock Around the Clock*. Man, I thought, I wish I could dance to that. Sharon spotted me and must have understood what I was thinking. She walked over and asked, "Want to dance?"

"I'd like to try."

Just touching her hand and putting my hand on the small of her back was thrilling, but it was clear I had no sense of what to do.

"It's not a waltz," she said. "Don't think, just feel the beat and let your body move."

After a few minutes, I seemed to get it. At least, I felt the rhythm. And, it was fun!

There was a freedom in dancing that made the experience wonderfully physical. I didn't feel like Alice would abandon me and leave me alone on the floor. It was a sort of boy-girl commitment. But if she did, I would just be thankful for the moment and movement together and that was all right, too.

"Thanks a lot," I said as the bell rang and we rushed off to class. But I couldn't stop thinking about dancing and the power of performance.

It later occurred to me that dancing, like so many other things in life, is made up of two opposing, yet complementary, notions. One has to do with technique and the second with artistry. Dance is about understanding rhythm, step, movement, and interpretation—about techniques. But dance is also a flow of elements that go far beyond technique and approaches artistry.

When the dance is over, it's over. All we have left is the memory of the quality or the regret of not doing our best.

The Knight Chlovly said, "It's a performance." The regrets of life are almost always about not giving your best quality performance when the opportunity is presented. But doing your best is most often a feeling and that's why we also need technique. We can practice technique, and even measure it. But in the game, in the dance, in life, there is little satisfaction in only knowing skills.

Satisfaction comes from the subjective gestalt of art, which includes skills, but is much more. We must see the field and ourselves on it, and make our own contribution to the game, moving it toward beauty. I am conscious of only a few true artists in the several skill areas that cross my mind. No matter who you consider—the teacher, the baseball player, the father, the actor…only a precious few are artists.

Art has a great deal to do with the ability to see. Aesthetics has everything to do with perspective or seeing yourself in relationship to others, to the deep values of the culture, and to the consequences of behavior. Artistry is also about seeing, seeing, feeling, and articulating relationships within the contemporary networks in which we work and live. In a relatively short time, I would be selected to play on the varsity basketball team. This achievement had to do with an improving skill level; but it had much more to do with my ability to see—to see my relationship to the others on the basketball floor—to conceptualize the game and see the whole thing in my mind, and to understand my reciprocal duty to the other players on the floor. I simply stopped my self-focus and in that moment, I added quality to the team.

The good athlete brings together two assumptions that form a theory of team and sportsmanship, which I call 'shared duty' — knowing that my self-interests are dependent upon the interests of others.

32

QUALITY ENGAGEMENT IN LIFE IS ALWAYS an issue here. In our lives, we perform many roles, but roles are meaningless without responsibility. And, responsibility comes from a deep understanding of the identity and honor related to that role.

If we play the role of neighbor, then we find and feel mutual safety and respect. We can count on each other. And, because we are members of a larger political democratic community, citizenship becomes the nucleus of our many other roles. Being a good athlete or citizen of a team means a moral attachment to others and other institutions. Even in so-called individual sports, the isolate is doomed. As we know, though, social relationships are intricate, subtle in their social constructs and information sharing, and extremely slow in developing—how like a great athletic program or a good family.

Two ideas or assumptions are important to achieve harmony between the one and the many. First, moral and material infrastructures, from health and education, to assumptions about truthful public dialogs are all necessary conditions for athletic success, or for success in any field or occupation. However, the sufficient condition for the quality of a family, a firm, or a team, is the individual's attitude and understanding of self-interest. Within any group, formal or informal, the individual and the association must see their wellbeing as mutually dependent.

The citizen of any organization carries a personal or private mind-set that demands being a loving critic of that group and a creator of both common and private wealth, where wealth is understood as the creation of excellence. The individual must simply be willing to help others be better, in order to live in a better family, neighborhood, or country.

The second assumption, which is public or system-wide in nature, concerns the relationships among institutions. This assumes that in a democratic republic, the several institutions that operate in a community, understand and practice reciprocal duties with one another. It also asserts that the individuals within are citizens of all the institutions to which they belong. That is, an individual is a citizen of the family, school, firm or business, place of worship, basketball team, etc., as well as the city, state, and nation.

If people do not see themselves as citizens of the institutions in which they work, play, learn, and live, it is problematic as to whether they can be citizens of a city, state, or nation. Once we understand this multidimensional engagement, we can embrace the ethics of reciprocal duty, which is the hallmark of citizenship and of championship teams. The citizen, as a member of the family or basketball team, seldom asks the family or team to do things for him or her, but how he or she can serve the team or family—that is, make the family or team better. In working to make the family or team better, the person will be better—it's that simple.

One of the problems we have in thinking about and implementing the idea of multidimensional engagement is the way in which we have marginalized the role of citizen, even the citizen of the team. The citizen of the basketball team, for example, understands that playing defense is a cooperative behavior, and takes joy in working together. An individual can create an irresistible idea but making a performance from that idea takes a team effort.

"Team" will always beat "individual." It has been proven over and over again. Teams comprised of citizens can always beat teams made up of subjects who only know how to play for themselves. Defense, passing, and team patterns will almost always beat the hoggish individual star. However, when individuals think about being citizens, they often think about this as something extra in their normal life. It's an add-on that they believe will demand extra effort, time, and resources in an already jam-packed existence, and will only diminish their individual specialty.

Citizenship, however, is not an add-on to the activities of life; it is the essential attribute, mindset, or glue among the many roles we play as we participate in all facets of life. It's the system or web of rules, morals, and affections that brings meaning to human constructs and life itself. Citizenship improves individual effort because of mutual support. Someone has my back.

Regardless of the institution, citizens busy themselves creating wealth or excellence in all of the institutions in which they live, work, and play, while subjects cling to the role of consumer, believing that they are entitled to receive wealth from those same institutions.

Citizens understand that there can be no private wealth without common wealth. That is, making the team better will make each player better. Again, what has to be clear is the idea that one should be a citizen of all the institutions in which he or she is engaged. It is simply an overarching identity, not an add-on. It is the governor of our identity.

The secret to wealth and excellence is the knowledge of how citizens come together from different institutions in different community configurations. That is, citizens of different families will or should cross paths at work, in church, at the Rotary Club, at the city recreation basketball league, and other venues. In this mix, people learn how and why institutions develop reciprocal duties with each other. And from this mix, championships are won. The true citizen can never say, "I was just following orders." People who cannot understand relationships and reciprocal duty or who tend to focus on one vision or one master might be followers or subjects of any master, simply because they reject reason.

In the end, better families do make for better schools; better communities make for better students and athletic teams; better businesses influence governments positively; better religious institutions help create better service clubs, and on and on. Citizens of institutions share democratic responsibilities with members of other organizations. Indeed, individuals who understand this notion of reciprocal duty will enhance all institutions and the health of the community as well. This is the case because the community is simply the aggregate of institutions therein. The character of the team is created from this seedbed.

The concept of the limited good is a foreign idea to the creation of excellence and to democracy. Within the democratic context, the citizen works to grow the good instead of maintaining the moral and economic inadequacies that diminish happiness. This notion of citizenship is the essence of quality. If we understand the true nature of public happiness as members of an athletic team, we will succeed.

33

As the Tuesday before Thanksgiving approached, I became more anxious about our first basketball game. Monday's easy practice went well, and I felt comfortable about starting on the JV team. We ran through defensive and offensive patterns against the varsity and with Jerry, our star sophomore, playing with us, we gave the varsity all they could handle.

Tuesday morning chores were a blur and, for the most part, so were my classes. At 3:30, we suited up for the pep rally in our white home uniforms. My numbers are 30 for home games and 31 for away. I wanted number 13, but there was no 13. Superstition. At the first basketball pep rally, Coach introduced both teams and said that we would be great competitors this year.

"These guys have worked hard and will represent you well this year. If they can count on your support, we will all be winners."

We had a short meeting as we changed back into our street or school clothes. Keith's brother drove us home. I had time to boil an egg, make some toast, and eat quickly before I checked on things in the barn, carried milk out to the milk-house, and said good-bye to Happy.

I ran back to the house, discarded my barn clothes for something better, and was back in the yard at 6:00 just as Keith and his brother drove in. We were off to town.

In the 1950s, during the cold months from November to March, small towns in Wisconsin were hotbeds of high school basketball. All of New Kassel and people from miles around came to watch the best show in town. It was, of course, the only show in town. Few people had TVs, the movie theaters were busy on weekends, but in the winter, on Tuesday and Friday nights, the entertainment center was the high school gym. After the Friday night games, there would always be a sock-hop with a disk jockey sponsored by a local business.

We got to the gym at 6:20, and even though the JV game wouldn't start for another half hour, the stands were already full. Other people were in the lobby and in the halls, and the band was on stage playing marches and school songs interspersed with pop music. The smell of popcorn hung in the air and gave a circus feeling to the affair that elevated the excitement of the whole event. I was caught-up in the clamor, the romance, and the drama. I loved it!

By 7:00, we were dressed in our white home uniforms and took the floor, adored by the home crowd and jeered by the visitors, mostly in good fun. This was just a warm-up game for the varsity but, still, the crowd was invested.

After our pre-game preparations, Coach told the starters what defense we would play and that we should only run the first option of our offensive pattern. He started three freshmen— Tom, Keith, and me—one sophomore, Jerry; and one junior, Don—who was very thin and looked younger but taller than the freshmen, and everyone believed he had potential.

At the center of the now-packed gym, I felt small and our whole team looked small, too. The noise was so loud that I couldn't hear what Jerry was saying to me. As the other team took the floor, I could see that we were taller than they, and the guy guarding me barely came up to my chin. In the noise and blur of the crowd, I couldn't remember anything about what to do on the court. As Jerry got ready to jump-center, all I can think is, "Focus, focus, focus!"

Jerry easily got the jump and tipped it back to me. I had the ball and instinctively passed it ahead to Tom, who had stationed himself on the side of the court at the extension of the free-throw line. Jerry broke down the keyhole, receiving Tom's pass and gracefully laid the ball off the backboard.

Boy! That was fast. I was still moving toward our basket when their center took the ball out of bounds. As he threw it to his guard, I intercepted the ball and laid it back in. 4, zip!

The game was ours from those first two baskets. Jerry and Keith dominated the backboards and the two of them had more rebounds than the entire other team. We found it easy to run fast-breaks and we all scored at least one lay-up. I ended the game with 9 points, Tom, Keith, and Jerry had 10, 6, and 15 points, respectively—as was reported in the town paper on Wednesday. The final score was 46 to 35. We won our first game. The varsity lost.

By the fourth game of the season, both Jerry and I were moved up to the varsity and to this day, I try to figure why. With Jerry, it was clear. He was just that good. I, on the other hand, was just beginning to learn the game. If there was anything to account for the move, perhaps it had something to do with my ability to see the court better and understand that basketball was a game of straight lines connected by ninety-degree angles. The shortest distance was, indeed, a straight line and not a curve. I also changed my thinking. I was becoming a citizen of the team—interested in the common good. Yep, I had changed my view. It certainly was not my body that made me a varsity player, although I was finally starting the growing spurt that adolescent boys pass through. I was at least an inch taller now than I had been last summer. But that wasn't it. It was my mind, or better said, my ability to see. Just a few weeks ago, I could only envision myself. That is, I could only think about my position on the floor and not very well at that. There was no sense of my relationship with others, with the situation on the floor, with the difference between practice and the game. That was all changing.

One day in practice as I brought the ball down court against the varsity, I saw everything. I mean everything. I could see all of my teammates, where every defensive player was, and whether he was standing or moving and, best of all, the action on the court seemed to have slowed down. From that moment, my mental ability to play basketball changed.

Coach noticed immediately and as the practice went on, others did as well. My passes were better, even good. I could set up our players for easy shots and could score myself. When you can see, the game comes to you. You simply know how to react to the changing nature of the thousand situations that are possible every moment.

You don't fight the dynamic of the circumstances; you make the situation suit you. I suspect that everything we learn that's really important is about seeing and understanding relation-ships. Whether basketball or basket-weaving, physics or psychology, understanding the discipline of any field of study or endeavor is actually about the relationships we see and connect.

If you don't know the major ideas, logic, and applications of biology, for example, you simply can't comprehend the subject, no matter how well you can read. Likewise, you can't be a good basketball player if you don't know the fundamental ideas, skills, logic, and their applications in the game, no matter how well you can dribble or shoot.

In both cases, it is a matter of seeing the relationships between knowledge and application. Both are about thinking, but thinking with and within the integrity of a particular discipline. I believed, and may still, that comprehending biology may help a person become a better basketball player. It deepens your thinking skills as it were, but that is true if, and only if, you comprehend basketball, too. Like biology, basketball is a discipline. If you don't understand that, you simply won't be a citizen or scholar of the game, to say nothing of being an artisan.

I wanted to be an artisan of this game and I was beginning to understand what that meant. Doing something right is meaningless if you don't do the right thing in context. Rightful behavior is a matter of two things: knowing the good and doing the good.

Like any relational activity, basketball provides a context for behavior and you can see what the right thing is, but to then do it —now that's something. The lesson was clear; being able to perform skills is meaningless unless you can use those skills to do the right thing. And the right things are relational. Rationality is necessary, but there was something more.

Through rationality and observation, I see the other players. And, the reality I see is also in my mind. It is enhanced by my ability to build connections, and my desire to see others and higher principles, like honor, in meaningful communication with others. Only the individual can make an ethical decision when confronted by one, but one cannot be moral alone. Perhaps I was learning to make proper decisions because I now saw more completely, and for that, I was moved up to varsity.

We commonly assume that our conscious experience is a direct awareness of objects and events in the external world. Most of us believe that our senses mirror the world exactly, and that our sensory neural pathways somehow transmit copies of it to the brain. It's more than that, and I was beginning to find this out on the basketball floor. Sure, I could see the basket when shooting the ball, but making a basket was a contextual feeling. Yes, we do "see" with our eyes and use our other senses, but in a larger way we "see" beyond our senses.

I was seeing the larger context; the relationship between significance and seeing. In short, I was bringing meaning to my game because I was seeing more with my mind. Things became more clear. We classify or carve up the world with our mind; our paradigms, our precepts, and our mysteries, and meaning will hold only to a unifying framework that embraces all of this. I was now working from a new framework. Out of mind, out of sight is more accurate that the converse.

34

CHRISTMAS WAS COMING. MARK WAS not. Mama called and said that she would be home a week before the holiday, but Mark would stay in Chicago, stay in school, and would come back in the spring after school was out. Why? Mark could certainly live here. What was she afraid of?

I often wondered what the reasons were for her attraction to Chicago. Her take on it was that she was working there to help pay off the mortgage. But I think the truth was somewhere, or perhaps someone, else. I think that it also had to do with her identity, her sense of place. She was two different people. She disliked the person who lived on the farm. So, she didn't.

She was out of her element here. Sure, the work was hard, but it wasn't about the work. It was about the relationships she had in Wisconsin in contrast to the ones in Chicago. We see ourselves, our identity, in the eyes of friends. With few friends, the image may be weak. Finding and keeping friends takes work, and for Mama, at her age, she wasn't about that sort of work. Her friend-keeping energies were easier in Chicago.

While identity has a great deal to do with friends, it has even more to do with location and circumstance. And, where location and circumstance meet, we find the opportunity for friendship, marriage, vocation, and even faith. But identity, more than anything else, is an invention. It's created with attention to circumstance, opportunity, and through love. It is pure romance—all self-created identities are. We all build these signatures for ourselves, our families, our schools, our community, our nation, and they are all created out of perceptions and validated through environmental experimentation and achievement.

For many of us, identity is made more real though experimentation. Others never do the work to make identity real. The lucky ones among us put more attention on the achieving, but they are both there, the good with the bad, the perception with the fact. Identity depends on friends, on location, on circumstance, on achievement, and most of all on our imagination and courage. I could see all of this in Mama's ambivalence about staying on the farm. The farm had its own wonder, but it was so subtle that you had to look hard to find it.

What Mama lacked was the courage to build a new identity related to the circumstances of the farm, and in the future, Mark and I would suffer because of her timidity. I did because I couldn't grasp the importance of place and circumstance, believing they were easy constructs devoid of struggle. I'm not sure about Mark.

Three days before Christmas, Happy and I drove the pickup truck over the snow-packed road and down to our summer pasture in search of a Christmas tree somewhere between the pasture and the swamp that stretched for about a mile toward the southwest. The little stream that ran through the swamp was lined with cedars, some hemlocks, Norway pines, and balsams.

The trees were heavily covered with snow, so it was hard to evaluate their Christmas-tree potential.

We walked for about twenty minutes before I left the stream and clambered up a steep hill where I spotted a nicely proportioned spruce. It was a one-of-a-kind and we both knew immediately that this was the tree. Happy let me saw it down, all eight feet of it, and we carried it back to the truck arriving home as quickly as possible and with anticipation regarding how pleased Mama would be with this beauty.

We cut off about a foot or so from the bottom of the tree and set it up in the living room. The following evening, we decorated it. The tree seemed really big, much bigger than any tree we had ever had before. It was beautiful even if there were scarcely any lights and ornaments for it. We strung some popcorn and cranberries—that helped. As I remember it now, it defines Christmas trees for me, none since has been that gorgeous. The smell of evergreen in the house in December pushes me right back to that tree and that day, and the sadness I had over missing family that Christmas.

Christmas Eve was frigid. The thermometer outside of the milk-house at 5:30 said 23 below zero. After chores, the three of us quickly cleaned up, changed into our best warm clothes and went to church, the Lutheran Church, perhaps, as a nod of approval to me, but more likely it was for their famous candle-light service. This has remained a favorite Christmas memory. Upon entering the church, each person was given a small candle and toward the end of the service, before the singing of familiar carols, ushers would light the candle of the person standing on the aisle who would lean to light the candle of the next person and all down the row until all the candles in the pew were lit. Soon, every candle throughout the church flickered.

The sight was glorious and the singing joyful. After about twenty minutes of song, people walked slowly from the church service and many of them continued to walk down the streets, for a block or two, singing carols to the people and families inside the well-lit houses. I joined them for a song or two and then got into the car with Mama and Happy for a pleasant ride home. We were each quiet and content knowing that Christmas had enjoyed a good start, even without Mark.

There was a melancholy to Christmas that maybe comes from the persistent Wisconsin cold, gray sky in December, or maybe from missing people not here or long gone, or maybe from struggling to know what Christmas is really about. I'd always been told that Christmas was about Christ's birthday. That was clear and I had no reason to debate it. Christmas was about going to church and not about presents under the tree. There were few presents; I received two that year. There were few things to confuse the issue; yet, I did feel confusion, especially about the melancholy.

Being confused is not always a bad thing. Faith is based on confusion. You don't need faith if you are certain and without doubt. Faith is for those of us unclear about the mysteries of life, death, God, love, and fear. That Christmas, I had plenty of doubt and needed to cling to some sustaining idea. The idea could not be Mama. It could not be the land. It could not be God. I knew almost nothing about these things, and least of all about myself. What could I turn to? Who?

Was basketball sustaining? Was the love of family enough of a support for me? If, indeed, I had one. Was the thought of being better in the future helpful? What I would come to realize was that the sustaining elements of life are in the right relationships we build with one another, and I was in trouble for lack of know how. Life is like a web that radiates out to connect with others. And, the larger the network, the more opportunities for sustainability. The core of these relationships, of course, is love.

We didn't talk much about these things in class, although many students would have liked to. We could sense, however, when things were not well with the nation and, by extension, with ourselves. Things were changing, even here in northern Wisconsin. In spite of these changes. It seemed that our parents were turning us free. They had given so much through the Depression and WWII that maybe they thought it was time to live our own lives.

People were leaving cities for suburbs; streetcars, trains, and buses gave way to the automobile, and in the evenings, more people began to watch TV than talked to neighbors. Mama could no longer take the train from our farm to Chicago.

I've often found it difficult to understand the line from L. Frank Baum's *The Wizard of Oz:* "A heart is not judged by how much you love, but by how much you are loved." On the face of it, it just sounds lazy. Being loved, at one level, is pretty easy. You may be loved and remain passive. Passivity in love is something to be suspicious about. Is it disrespectful to be loved without loving? Happiness is being kind and thoughtful enough that people will love you. It's being lovely. We show our love for others by our behavior toward them, and in that engagement, we are loved. Something I would like to believe, but life has taught me that that is not always true. One can show love in different ways. There is no one definition of love. You'll know it when you see it – not always true.

I wonder about love regarding my mother or teachers. I think that loving is harder than being loved. It means embracing something that is so complex it may take a lifetime to understand. But with faith you proceed. The truly lucky are those who seem to be loved and can also love without thought or effort. They are lucky because it is in living between loving and being loved that we explore all that is meaningful and sustaining. They also know, as should we all, that sustainability never is, but always is to be. I have never experienced such love.

35

SPRING COMES FIRST TO THOSE FIELDS plowed last fall. The black soil drinks in the late March warmth, announcing with sweet aromas the start of a new season. As the snow recedes from the fields to pastures, then to the forests, you can assess the cadence of the ascending sun and begin to catalog spring's tasks.

First, an evaluation is made of the equipment needed for preparing the fields: plow, disks, drags, grain-drill, corn planter, and, of course, both of our tractors. The tractors were used throughout the winter to move snow, haul wood, and sometimes to pull cars out of snowbanks, but with spring planting, they will be in service for eight hours a day. We couldn't afford to have a breakdown.

By early April, if the rains or late snowstorm hold off, we disk and drag the first fields, preparing them for oats and the accompanying hayseeds of alfalfa, some clover, an assortment of timothy, and even broom grass—the latter especially for its color, which will add a golden glow to the hay fields two summers hence. The oats and hay seeds are "drilled" into the earth with a complement of commercial fertilizer. We are happy if, by mid-April, the oat fields are all seeded.

By late April, we have to prepare the corn fields, which will be planted by early or mid-May. The timing for planting corn is always a sparring match with any late frost. Sometimes you win, sometimes it snows. At this time of year, snow is better for the land than frost without snow, or so it seems to me. The corn fields are meticulously prepared; the planting bed must be marked with the straight lines of a surveyor's eye. If any row is bent or crooked, cultivating or dragging out the weeds later in the spring and summer will prove costly. There is pride that comes with looking back at a beautifully planted field. By May's end, the crops are in and one can look forward to letting nature bloom.

More than any activity on the farm, planting is about faith. A kernel of seed corn growing into stalks of corn is wonder-filled. There's a harmony and peace in the act of planting. Perhaps it is just the season of spring, but I think it has more to do with envisioning what will happen in the interplay of soil, rain, seed, and faith...faith in the invisible process of life.

The farmer works so hard to clear fields of stones and weeds and has borrowed and spent a great deal of money and time preparing a seedbed that it seems appropriate to embrace faith. That is, seeing beyond sight and experimentation, because seeing with faith or beyond the surface structures is a necessary condition or attitude in this business. The farmer looks at the field and says, "I see you." Looking at and past the field, the farmer understands its every mood, and in this knowledge, finds some peace. There's a simple grace in this awareness. There's an uncomplicated intricacy in seeing relationships among the sun, rain, soil, and seed. There's also the knowledge that comes from seeing the whole in all its harmony. "I see you."

Without this ability to see, the farmer falls into incompetence, resulting in cruelty against the land, and in the end, against all of us. With vision, or better, with virtue, the farmer experiences peace, a peace only possible through competence.

Although left unstated, the farmer finds peace in a planted field and sees love as the seedbed of grain, as well as of happiness—simply a by-product of a well-prepared field. With a straw -sucking, sun-tanned smile, the farmer knows just how difficult all of this is to achieve, but each new planting gives a hint into this mystery and another chance to compete for the prize.

The small dairy farmer I refer to here is very different from the large farmers I call "miners." The new miners in Wisconsin, the ones I am talking about, are not the English, Welsh, or Italian "Badgers" of the old lead and zinc mines in the southwestern part of the state, but those thoughtless users of the soil who show no stewardship of the land and simply mine its soils. From what I have seen these many years since those first spring plantings of mine, I often wonder where conscience has gone. Perhaps it withered as the price of land increased and as big business, with government corporate welfare payments and tax breaks, bought up family farms and turned them into milk factories. Now we have dairy farms where one farm will milk 2,000 cows, three times a day. The cow never sees a pasture, and the land is poisoned so the corporation can get four hay crops in one summer, rendering the land useless to its natural calling. These are factories, not farms.

Beware of doing things just because you can.

The land has instinctive expectations. These expectations are within the natural tolerances of soil, rain, sun, seed, and stewardship. To push the land or cows beyond natural designs is a manifestation of blindness that disrespects reciprocal duty and ethics. Like the land, we are often put in similar binds when we feel we must live up, or down, to the expectations of others. Or even worse, when we embrace the expectations of others to the point where we come to believe that they are our personal expectations. As we should be reflective of our own expectations, so too we must respect the expectations of the land.

36

SPRING. SPRING IS ALSO BASEBALL'S TIME. Practice started in the high school gym while snow still covered the ground. I felt confident and would work hard to make the varsity team, either at shortstop or second base. Almost all the boys came out for baseball. There must have been forty or more guys out on that first day—everyone thinks they can play baseball. The farm boy who makes it all the way to the majors seems like a fairytale, but it happens. These were big, strong boys who would play catch all summer and could throw a baseball hard enough to put a dent in a wooden barn door.

Practice was filled with drills of running, catching, hitting a baseball on a rope, sliding practice, and more running. We ran, did push-ups, and threw the baseball the length of the gym trying to keep it not more than ten feet off the floor.

There were puddles, and often snow patches in the outfield, but by late March we began practicing outside. Everything was cold and seemed out of place. Baseball is a warm or even hot sport. You sweat a lot and the heat loosens muscles, so throwing, hitting, and running are smooth and easy. In Wisconsin, there's a late March chill that can put a sting into those activities. But it's baseball, hot or not, and more fun than anything else I can think of.

After two slow runs around the outfield, we were clocked running from home to first and then sprinting around the bases often through mud. We were all mud-covered as Coach took a bucket of balls halfway between the pitcher's mound and the backstop. He threw a rubber mat ten feet from the fence in front of the bleachers behind home plate, "Let's see if anyone of you can hit. Johnson, Baldwin, and Hartoonian, grab a bat," he said. "Hitters, bunt the first pitch, hit away on the next five, and run out the sixth. The rest of you line up to catch flies in the outfield. Gene, hit some flies to them."

I looked for a bat while Johnson and Baldwin hit first. We had a dozen or so new bats. They looked so nice that I didn't want to use any of them in this mud hole. I needed to pick one, though, so I settled on a Jackie Robinson. Maybe it was the cold weather and I wanted some protection for my hands. The Robinson bat has a thick barrel and that thickness diminishes very little right down through the handle. Any inside pitches would transfer less of a sting on the hands, I thought.

Coach was throwing pretty hard for batting practice. I stepped in and watched the first pitch come right down the pipe and did nothing.

"Bunt the ball!"

He threw again. I opened my stance to bunt and pop it up.

"Bring the bat here!"

I ran it out to Coach.

"Give it here."

He grabbed the bat and went through the motions of bunting.

"Face the pitcher, bend your knees, start with the bat belt high, hands apart—one on the handle, the other on the barrel. Hold the bat gently with your fingers protected behind the bat and move the bat slowly back and up to meet and cushion the ball, so you won't pop it up. The ball hits the bat, the bat does not hit the ball. Now go back and give it a try."

He threw a sweet one down the middle and the bunt was right where it should have been—rolling slowly down the third-base line. But more than that, it felt good.

It is one of the greatest pleasures in life to take an idea and execute it in reality. Of course, coming up with the idea isn't bad either. Baseball is all about ideas and performance.

Baseball has an interesting structure. There are three levels of participation: individual, team, and if it gets inside your soul, you have to participate in the history of the game. Like any game, it is defined by four elements. These include an irresistible idea, leadership, a willingness to work at play, and a collection of people who adhere to a more or less common set of principles and practices, with shared identities and responsibilities. With these attributes, you are a team. Leave out any one of the elements and you have a group, but not a team.

The idea of baseball is irresistible. It's like love, or justice, or even democracy. The place of baseball is prepossessing. Its geometry envisions a square that turns into a diamond, ninety feet on each side, with a raised mound, sixty feet, six inches from home plate. The diamond has grass within it and it is surrounded or encased by more grass, not just any grass, but freshly mowed grass, nature's true green.

The outfield is like a sublime pasture allowing freedom to run, to catch, and to throw. There is delight in chasing down a long fly and feeling it land with certainty in your glove. This grace of motion takes place because you intrinsically understand that the sound of the bat, hitting the ball, will predict the speed, distance, and the exact spot where the ball, sky, and glove will meet. As the white sphere arcs across a light blue sky, the several perfect shapes of art are expressed in play.

In baseball, home is where you start and you want to end. Getting there, however, is a difficult journey filled with danger and decisions. This idea of the journey from home across first, second, and third, and back to home is the human journey. It's the story of the human quest for adventure, glory, and treasure. You travel long and hard, most often by yourself. And, as in life, the journey takes its toll and can be very dangerous - a pitcher can throw a ball over 90 miles an hour just a few inches from your head. And like great literature and life, when you finally find your treasure or arrive home, it's not what you expected.

To get to first base, you must hit the ball into fair territory and run to first base before someone can catch the ball or throw you out. You are considered skilled, if you can reach or cross first base three out of ten times.

From first base, you are still a long way from home. And, now you must rely on others, on your team. You might be able to steal second base and even third, but your chances of advancing and reaching home are dependent on teammates who hit the ball safely behind you.

Playing, and certainly winning, depend on team members' ability to play the game well. Personal power is enhanced through connections with others. Your individual and team power depends on your knowledge of each other, and that means physical strengths, as well as mental tendencies. Your ability to help and share with each other determines the quality of the team. Baseball is an idea defined by human relationships. Back in the 1950s, baseball was America's game and in many ways, expressed values, such as a reverence for history and statistics, as well as the struggle for equality.

37

My freshman year came to an end with the end of baseball season. We played fifteen games, of which we won only six, leaving us with no tournament to look forward to. I won my varsity letter, playing second base and hitting .281. All in all, it was a mediocre season. Summer was just around the corner, and I needed to turn my attention to farm work, Legion baseball, the hometown, home-talent baseball league, softball games on Wednesday nights, and flirting with girls. It would be a full summer.

Mr. Close, our American Legion coach, greeted about twenty of us at the first practice. The Legion team represented the city of Centerville, which was by state population criteria, a city and not just a town like New Kassel. Several of us trying out for the team were from surrounding little towns and the home-city guys didn't welcome the fact that intruders might take their spots on the team. There were six of us intruders from two different towns. Four of us were kids, between our freshmen and sophomore years, one was going into his junior year, and one, although just 17, was between his junior and senior year.

The speech that Coach Close gave to us on that day so long ago has morphed into memory, yet the meaning of it was so powerful that I recall major elements of it to this day.

"Baseball, like life," he started, "is about the task at hand. You show up, you pay attention, and you damned well better focus. I don't care if you're in love, if your father drinks, if you have a million dollars, if you're... —I don't care. When you're on my field, I own you! You put baseball first. That's your task right now. By putting the task first, you move the focus away from yourself. Your first thought is to get over yourself! Push those thoughts of yourself away. Besides, you're too young to be anything than boring, and from what I can see, your knowledge of baseball is not only boring, but almost funny. Push your thoughts away from your petty expectations, your nerves, your ego, your 'look,' and just lose yourself in the job: hitting the ball, throwing the ball, catching the ball, and running. In life, as in baseball, there is little room and less time for excuses or 'poor me' thoughts—these are the feelings of little people. Show me a man who is full of himself and I'll show you an empty person. You want to be aware of yourself? The only way is to perform in front of people who understand the game—whatever that game happens to be. Hang around with people who know what they're doing and you'll learn any game and a lot about yourself. I don't want little people on my field. If you see beyond yourself and into the task at hand, you will be winners."

He took us all over to home plate.

"Focus on the task! In this box, there is no thinking about the past or future, just the task of hitting the ball. In the dugout, you concentrate on every aspect on the game in front of you. On the field, you focus on the tasks at hand by thinking ahead. How will this guy hit a curve? A fast ball? Should I play him a shade to the right? So, you are not important—hitting the ball is! Focus calls for discipline, which will lead you to the freedom to play your best game. You focus, you work, you perform, and you'll win, even if you lose the game."

Coach Close was the best coach I ever had—ever. And the next summer, he would have me starting at second base in the state all-star game, a game in which I hit a single, double, and triple. The double came off a young man who was scouted and signed by the Yankees. With that one hit, I began to be noticed outside of New Kassel and Centerville as well.

It's funny how one event, one person, one action can change everything. I only spent two seasons with Mr. Close, and as I later thought about coaches, mentors, or parents, I began to see how they can improve your life with nothing more than the truth—the truth about you and the truth about the world. And the core of that truth is to simply say, you can do this or that, but it will take courage, hard work, time, focus, and a sense of what you're up against.

That real world cannot be created out of ignorance, fear, or a feeling of victimization. And whatever that world is, it will never hold happiness if you stop short of competence. Without intellectual, physical, and spiritual competence, you will forever be angry with yourself and often with others as well.

The position you play in life is not important, be that position pitcher, president, or parent. What is important is that you are competent at what you do and that you take no shortcuts to achievement. Status given means nothing. Status earned is all. It's a simple truth, often not learned.

There were baseball groupies even back in the fifties. In this case, they were high school girls from Centerville overly interested in the boys on the Legion team. Today, I can't think of anything more boring than a group of teenage baseball players from small-town Wisconsin, but the girls saw something there and they came at us with all the grace of baby birds learning to fly. I thought nothing of them as they watched practice. There was, however, a lesson headed my way—one I have relearned many times.

I thought that when it came to girls, there was a large space, a Grand Canyon, between the workings of a teenage boy's mind and the real world. Girls are different, I thought. They look, smell, behave, and perhaps, even think in different ways. To understand girls, you need to find out more. What's on their minds? What's under their dresses? What would it be like to touch them in regions never seen or touched before? And, you can't get these questions out of your head, no matter what Coach Close said about focus.

In the years since, what I have come to understand better is that relationships among people are based on common expectations about all kinds of things from food to values about politics, love, children, and even God. The sharing of values often makes you feel comfortable, and you try to find or build that commonality with friends. This was hard for me as I had no examples of how to proceed. And with girls, it seemed impossible.

We are taught that the beginning of wisdom is the fear of the Lord. And that simply means the ability to say "no." But as teenagers, we are damned confused about what it is that we should say no to. If we could understand our true nature and the lessons of history, we would aim some of our no's at the obnoxious and interfering structures of society and its institutions. In any worthy institution, the only rational idea is to ratchet down structure and ratchet up freedom—and to do it within a context of respect and mutual learning.

Instead, we are afraid of each other and even ourselves. We fear our bodies, our minds, our children, and our instincts. We don't really talk to each other. We are taught to beware of differences, not to think too hard about the church, government, and media, and not to concern ourselves with the plight of others. Can we really control our behavior without cultural sanctions? Can we be self-governing without responsibilities to others?

It is true that culture is something we create; something we destroy; something that protects us; and something that can victimize us. Culture is a tension between what is and what ought to be. Between what I want and what is good. You give up a great deal to live in culture, but there should be a return for your "investment." Culture carries sanctions that prevent certain behaviors deemed inappropriate, and encourages behaviors that reflect the culture's values. The values and behaviors esteemed in one culture are often frowned on in another culture. I guess the opposite of a profound truth is another profound truth. All of this is confusing to the young, but as a society, we say very little to our children about it.

We seem to have vast and powerful tensions between lust and love; happiness and desire; self and others; competition and cooperation. The stories and values we read about, hear, and see in the movies are not the things I feel and experience in my life.

The community, whether manifested in a mother, the church, or school tells us to be happy by giving of yourself to others and keeping our desires in check. But for some reason, I believe that if I am competing and winning, healthy and hand-some, and able to purchase a few of the things that I desire; then I am happy. Certainly, happier than I would be if I were sick, poor, ignorant, and lost at every game I played.

Maybe to truly understand people, or myself, I have to understand contrasts and tensions. There is a juxtaposition of geography, of language, and of perception within any meaning-ful communication. We will talk right by each other if we believe that we all have the same perspective.

Culture can never be static, or it dies. That is the case with talking, loving, dining, working, learning, governing; relation-ships all. And these relationships are always dynamic. We often hear, "If you don't use it, you lose it." Perhaps what is more to the point is the fact that if you don't use it in a better way, you lose it.

We lose appetite, sex, knowledge, and meaning by hearing the same tired old stories and by doing the same damned things over and over again. Yes, communication is about seeing and doing the same old things, but in new or different contexts. It is about refreshing our traditions so change becomes a gentle constant in our life. If we don't become loving critics of tradition and work to change our behavior with one another, relationships die, even good relationships.

The big problem with relationships between teenaged boys and girls is that they have little to do with cultural DNA or with rational debates that we might prefer in our society. These first sensual relationships have to do with animal discoveries and illusion.

38

Uncle Vartin told me once that the most precious time of life is the time you can waste. And I understood that in my running, in reading, and even in playing. That summer before my sophomore year, however, I thought I was too busy to waste anything—energy, thoughts, or time. Looking back, I realize that he was right; I wasted much of the summer, and happily.

By June, we were into the swing of farm chores and field work. The cows, the crops, and my muscles testified to that every day. I also had to earn some spending money to buy treats after ballgames at Centerville, some clothes for myself, and a single-shot 20-gauge shotgun that I coveted, offered for sale at the hardware store for $24. There was no chance of earning money at home; the work was just expected. I would have to think of something else.

Mark was home now and would do more than his share of farm work, as well as play softball on Wednesday nights with me. He also found a neighbor who had a bean and cucumber field and was looking for pickers—half-a-cent a pound for beans; a quarter-a-cent for five pounds of cucumbers. In the time we could afford, we picked for about two weeks before deciding that the $10 we made between us during that time was not enough, so we looked for something else.

Mark found a job for a week hauling cedar posts for one of our neighbors and also did some babysitting. I found nothing, but admittedly, Mark looked harder.

One thing that we liked to do besides play ball was go to the local dances held in every town within the five surrounding counties. These were polka and waltz dances with some new rock'n'roll thrown in from time to time. Mark loved the rock, while I favored the polkas, at least at first. With the waltz or polka, you could hold a girl, and it was happy music.

At one of the dances, an opportunity presented itself that got me directly involved in music. Betty, one of the polka band leaders had just bought the local Dew-Drop-Inn. Because she had a band, she changed the name of the tavern to the Acord-de-Inn. Lame, I know, but that's what she named it. Her band, patterned after the famous polka band leader, Frankie Yankovic, had two accordions. She played one accordion, but the guy who played second accordion was leaving the area. One day, when Happy and I stopped by her tavern, a habit for Happy, she approached me and asked if I would be interested in playing in the band. She knew of my interest in music—singing in the church and high school choruses, able to read music a little, and attending many of her dances. I told her I didn't play any musical instrument, but she insisted that I could learn to play the accordion by next spring and being 16 years old by then, would be able to stay at the dance until 1:00 a.m. I would have from July or August until next May.

"You can do it!" she said. "I'll pay you $15 a dance and you would play with us once a week, all summer long, until school starts."

It didn't take long to add up those numbers, and I said I would, not knowing anything about what I was getting into.

There was a music store in Centerville, and the owner taught kids to play the accordion, among other instruments. That night, I called Mama in Chicago and asked if we could rent an accordion so I could take a few lessons. She thought that it would be fine and would send some money as soon as she could.

With anticipation, Happy and I went to Centerville to look at the accordions and sign up for some lessons. The rent on a used accordion was ten dollars for June and July, and lessons were two bucks each—I would plan to take two in June and four or five lessons in July and maybe August. Mrs. Hanson thought that by then, I would know if I wanted to go further, that is, take more lessons and buy my own instrument. I told her what I had in mind—playing in the band and all—and she said I could take the $10.00 rent money for June and July and apply it to the cost of the accordion and just keep it until I could pay for it in full, which would be $105 minus the rent, or $95.

That was a lot of money, and if I didn't make the band, I would be paying for this thing a long time. Nevertheless, I told Happy that I would work at it and by spring, I could be making $15 or so a week for at least ten weeks, or $150. He agreed and gave Mrs. Hanson ten dollars plus another two for my first lesson, right there and then. Happy walked over to the bar across the street saying he would be back in forty minutes.

Mrs. Hanson brought me a piano accordion, black with some silver detailing. It looked nice, even handsome. She showed me how to hold it, where to place my hands, and went over the way the base buttons and piano keyboard worked.

The accordion is a wind instrument. It has a bellow. For it to make a sound, you must push and pull with your left, or bass, hand to provide the necessary wind. If you stop, the sound stops. She asked me to play some notes on the piano or right-hand side and then on the bass, or left-hand side, pulling and pushing all the time. I made some noise and after a minute or so, she asked me to stop, then opened a music book and said that I needed to be able to read notes to turn noise into music. She noted that my ability to read music was weak and explained the things I needed to know before our next meeting in two weeks.

"The lines on the sheet music," she explained, "all had letter names (E G B D F) and the spaces between also had names (F A C E)."

I would need to know these notations as well as the meaning of Middle C and play a few scales, which I was to learn in two weeks.

"That's not all," she said. "You must also learn the meaning of staff signatures and the time value of notes. If you practice enough, you'll be able to do this in two weeks, and then I will teach you. If not, just bring the instrument back, I'll return your money, and we'll call it a day."

"Clear enough," I said, and Happy and I left for home with an accordion in its case on the front seat between us.

I did learn to play the scales, but reading the notes came slowly, although I had no problem with the left hand or bass notes. Mrs. Hanson was pleased with my progress and agreed to work with me at least until school started.

That summer and through my sophomore year, I worked hard each day at learning music and within a few months, I could play several songs from Yankovic's polka song book. That summer and into the fall, I began to love my time with the accordion. The sound got better and once I could read the music, it was almost magical. My playing began to actually sound, well, ok. By October, I was sitting in on Betty's rehearsals and learned a bit more and a bit different each week. Just maybe, by the following summer, I would be on the stage with the band.

Although we didn't know it, life was now becoming far too busy and more complex. Mark and I did all that we had to: chores, housework, schoolwork, accordion practice, athletics, church, a dance or movie now and then—and believed that that was just the way of things.

One night after milking and dinner, after dishes were washed, we sat, dog tired, at the kitchen table. Mark said that we should find way to be efficient in our work and more energetic.

For several weeks, we talked about it, but ended up agreeing that being energetic was something you were or were not. We did, however, agree to be more efficient about all our work. We would be patient and diligent. That was our deal. That was our wish anyway. Of course, wishing or even writing down a practice and actually practicing until the practice is habit is completely different. As Yogi Berra said, "In theory, there is no difference between theory and practice. In practice, there is."

39

CHANGE WOULD BE THE DOMINANT ELEMENT of my life during my sophomore year, and the year would have a different focus. There was still the isolation—small-farm, small-town, 1950s isolation. There was no TV in our house, only local radio, and the weekly Centerville newspaper. We were aware of the developing Civil Rights movement, the building of Interstate highways, and most of all, of suburbia. Some of our neighbors would still live in their old farm houses for years, but our farms would eventually be taken over, not so much by the urban sprawl that affected the larger cities, but by a different kind of suburbia caused by people who just wanted a second home, a hobby farm, or an investment in land.

By the late fifties, and right up until today, government farm policies, not the market, doomed the family farm. Price supports, keeping land out of production, and the escalating price of farmland, as well as the rising taxes, put the small farms in economic intensive care. Despite their rhetoric, the twenty- or thirty-cow and eighty-acre farm was just a theory or an abstraction to the politicians and policies coming from Madison and Washington.

The Land Bank? We couldn't take land out of production. As the price of land continued upward, the only reward we had was higher taxes. The winners were the corporate farms with hundreds of cows and thousands of acres. These guys made more money doing nothing—putting land in the Land Bank than working farmer made breaking their backs seven days a week, every week. But hey, the destruction of the small farmer through our government was a way to fulfill the American Dream. Democratic nations are always destroyed by ignorant citizens who no longer care about the 'common wealth,' only their own private wealth. To be sure, some of the blame must be put on the farmers themselves. They would not entertain the idea that the future would be different from the past.

What is so hideous here is the way the Ag industry, not the family farmer, captured the government though donating money and power to politicians. The little farms, the large inner cities, and small towns were milked by policies and taxes to subsidize the builders of the suburbs.

Suburbia resulted from the voracious demand for housing following World War II. We had the land; we had the people to purchase the land; we had the contractors to build the houses on the land; we had government subsidies to help finance infrastructure outside the city; and we had the desire to leave the city and return to the sentimental and nostalgic notion of owning a piece of land—the foundation of the American Dream. The farmers I knew could no longer hold land for sentimental reasons. They sold it.

What we saw was the state and federal governments playing Robin Hood by taking tax revenues from the cities and small farmers, and using them to support the building of the suburbs. Millions were made by the few, because the government played favorites. After the 1960s, family farmers, who historically supported progressive policies, became bitter about the direction of America. They needed someone or something to blame, as opposed to being accountable. They saw things from their perspective, and began not to trust those 'elites' in Madison and Washington D.C. From the exchange of streetcars for buses to the financing of suburban infrastructure at the expense of the inner city, the rationales seem straightforward, but these policies decisions were short-sighted and we are paying dearly for them today. Perhaps the farmers were right.

The development of suburbs around American cities since WWII and over the last half of the 20th century is rooted in four controlling myths of the American culture. The centerpiece belief is the American Dream of land ownership. There was so much land in America that everyone could and should have a lot, a farm, or an acre on which to live and live out the dream. Of course, those of us with few resources or minorities might find it hard to dream this dream. We also wanted to live in smaller communities without any of the problems found in large cities. White people might say, "It's a real jungle in there." To save our Jeffersonian birthright, we had to start over, outside the ugly city. We never did understand the etymology of city: civilization, civic, civil, citizen.

Second, the notion that Americans are rugged individualists with a right to free movement was strongly at play. In the late 1950s, individualism and freedom were seen and defined in the automobile. There was a boom of car ownership after the war. The automobile better allowed the individual to be rugged and to own land, even the land far away from work and parents. The automobile also fit the new American business model of planned obsolescence. Many people started buying new cars every year or so. And, the new cars and roads favored building less dense housing patterns around the city at the expensive of those living in the city. City taxes were used to transfer commonwealth in the form of infrastructure construction from the city to the suburbs, so the fairy tale of individualism continued. With the passage of each deer-hunting season, more and more Illinois hunters, rugged individualists all, would find their way into our forests and farmland often without asking permission. They would shoot our cows, our horses, and even one of our neighbors' cars was shot at while he was driving through his woodlot. The automobile brought it all.

Third, we believed that our cities were not important in this new economic structure. We could live in the suburbs and work in the city without any responsibility for the city's health. This led to a deep disregard for the people living in cities as well as for the conditions needed for civilization's existence. We forgot that there is no civilization without healthy cities. Cities are always the economic and cultural centers of a civilization.

Finally, there was the belief that individual houses could be self-sustaining, separated from traditional neighborhoods and community anchors, such as churches, stores, schools, and firms without harming the neighborhoods. Some people even wanted to live "off the grid." The myth of self-sustainability destroyed the city neighborhoods, while failing to construct communities in the hinterlands. The delicate mix of institutions and the recipro-cal duty among them never caught on in most suburbs, and we were left with mile after mile of houses interrupted now and then by a strip mall or shopping center. Our own small town slowly died as more and more farmers left the land and the several newcomers did their shopping at the new malls or big box stores, so many miles away.

In the 1950s, we could just begin to see these trends, so there was no way to react to them. Not sure we would have reacted anyway. Such is the power of myth. It's too bad, but even well into the 21st century, its influence continues.

The basic reason that our primacy or classic institutions begin to fail, as they do from time to time, is because of a lack of cultural content. It's about the content, not the client or consumer. Professions such as teaching, law, medicine, theology, and others, should exist for an important reason: to protect the culture. That is, a culture creates professions to protect the dominant culture. Banker or baker, professionals must be concerned with their communities, and with the integrity of their content and the evaluation and advancement of that content onto the next generation. Through all professions, the city becomes a school. They are the teachers and people are educated by walking down the street or turning on a TV. We must ask, and the question is asked of us all: do we like what we're teaching?

By the late 1950s, it seemed as though many professionals began to give up their responsibilities and focus on a set of different values: materialism and individual power and wealth. Concerns and policies about inequalities of wealth—that is, the proper balance between private and commonwealth—and any thoughts about inequalities in education, law, or health were never heard above the noise of selfishness.

40

THAT SUMMER BEFORE MY SOPHOMORE year, I could feel change happening within me. While the barn chores and field work took on a familiar sequence, my body, mind, and relationships became more erratic and unfamiliar.

I started to notice my body, perhaps because it was changing so fast. A few straggly hairs appeared overnight on my legs and while I yet had little facial hair, I purchased a Gillette Blue Blade razor and a shaving cup, soap, and a face brush. Every Sunday, I'd shave, mostly without a blade in the razor. The soap made my face feel and smell clean. When I looked in the mirror without shirt or pants after a bath, I was embarrassed at just how skinny and awkward I looked.

Mark and I saw advertisements for Charles Atlas and his Dynamic Tension System in magazines and wanted to know the secret method of being Atlas-like. Even though Mark was powerfully built, we both felt like we should do something about our puny bodies so we sent away for the free explanation, but we didn't understand the routine. It seemed like all you did was push and pull on your arms and send money so we decided, without Coach's permission, to just make some dumbbells out of cement. We took some coffee cans and one-inch pipes and made several sets. We had to work fast before the cement set up. We filled the cans and the pipes and let them set over night. The next morning, before chores, we excitedly checked out our work and discovered that they were all too heavy for us to lift off the ground. And the pipes seemed to have disintegrated because of the cement inside them. We were the dumb bells.

Without Mama at home, our eating habits became more bizarre each week. Wheaties cereal, milk, toast, coffee, and an occasional trout or pork chop became our staples, not only for breakfast, but all of our meals. By September, Mark had finally had enough of our diet and he started to cook for us. The deal was that he would get some time off from outside chores or field work to cook.

Happy and I were pleased. We started to have beef roasts, chicken, and an occasional salad. It was all trial and error. Again, we dug potatoes, picked raspberries and put them in the freezer, wrapped apples in newspaper and put them in a barrel in the cellar, and with the beginning of hunting season and the fact that Happy butchered a pig and a male calf, we filled the freezer with beef, pork, venison, and berries, beans, and field corn.

We had little money to buy groceries, but as fall approached, our food supply enlarged and our meals got better. Mark got better and better and soon we started to have pot roast, beef stew, soups, and even spaghetti with meatballs. From those days to now, I have always appreciated good food and the people who could cook it. I began to look at Mark in a different way, and if the truth be told, in a deeper way, seeing talent inside of him that made him seem older than his years. Those meals didn't happen every day, but when they did, it made everything better. Cooking is an art that I never could master, and early on, gave up on it. It would seem that we had enough food and milk to never go without, but the days of going without would come back as they had in the past.

We also had to fill the basement with firewood. The wood-burning furnace would go through about five full cords each winter. One cord is two piles of 24-inch split firewood, four feet high and eight feet long, give or take. It took us about five days to prepare that much wood, which started by dragging dry treetops together. The trees had been cut for logs and sold to the lumber company at least two years ago. We would then take the slashings or leftover branches that were no good to the lumber yards and cut them into six- or eight-foot lengths. It took two people to lift these little logs up onto the saw-rig and cut into 24-inch firewood. We always cut more than we needed just in case any townspeople would want to buy some. It provided a little extra money for us.

On woodcutting days, Happy and I, and sometimes Mark, took the horses and tractor out to our woodlot about two miles from home. The horses would pull a wagon to carry the wood back and the tractor pulled the little circle-saw rig that Happy had built a few winters before. It ran off a belt that went from the tractor's power take-off pulley to the pulley on the saw–rig. We had painted it bright red and it looked new and beautiful against the fall colors. There's something special about being in the forest on a cool fall day. Such a day, warmed gently by the sun, makes the world seem clearer. The mix of cold air and warm sun, the turning colors of the maples, butternuts, ash, birch, and oaks, set off by the deep green of pines, punctuated by the lighter green of the pastures and rock-sown hills warmed my heart. It does still.

And, in these places, I am often overwhelmed by a feeling of loving the land. Every time since, when I experience this graceful mix of clime, color, and mood, I'm completely at peace, feeling so connected that my life, breath, cool air, and warm sun became the same. When I remember those times, I long for that feeling and wish that I could hold it again. This is what you get while harvesting firewood. It is true. Happiness and peace are simply by-products of paying attention and finding the joy in good, soul -healthy, work.

We couldn't handle the job by ourselves, so two or three neighbors would join us and help. We would either return the work or pay them with a load of firewood. This was dangerous work, especially for the person working the saw or throwing the newly cut wood into the box of the wagon. Happy would stand on a little platform on top of the rig and swing the saw with a long lever. Two people would feed the saw and the whole process had a rhythm—Happy leading the band of workers with the lever, feeders pushing eight-foot small logs into place, and me grabbing the now-24-inch, freshly cut pieces of wood and heaving them into the wagon.

None of us wore googles even though chips of wood and sawdust continually flew past our faces. Once the saw got into rhythm, everyone just tried to keep in step. It was efficient, but that's what also made it dangerous. The cadence could not be stopped on a dime, so we followed the rhythm carefully. The saw spinning a few inches from our bodies had no respect for off-beat syncopation and less for hands. We simply had to pay attention. Despite the attraction to do so, this was no place to daydream. At the end of the week, we had our five or more cords in the basement and more nicely piled and covered alongside the machine shed. Enough for us and some to sell.

The other fall tasks quickly fell into place—picking and husking corn, putting the field equipment in the shed, cutting the lawn for the last time, and whitewashing the inside of the barn and milk house. There was always another thing to do. Often, Mark and I would go to bed right after chores and dinner. In those weeks, we struggled to make time for schoolwork and for me, practicing the accordion became a matter of stolen moments. We hoped for rainy weekends when we could turn our attention to these pursuits, but they are rare in a Wisconsin autumn. With each passing day, however, more fall work would be completed, leaving time for our important activities—the things that we really wanted to do.

As the days and weeks flowed on into October, school began to dominate more of our time and as the temperature fell, we began to accommodate our farm work into the larger framework of our school life—classes, dances, football practice, accordion practice, and the occasional trip to the company store, the barber shop, and a movie. On one of those trips to purchase a pair of gym shoes, Mark and I experienced a hateful act that took us both by surprise.

While I was about to pay the five dollars and change for a new pair of shoes, Mark, now in eighth grade, saw some bubble gum behind the counter and stepped in front of me. "Can I have a piece of gum?"

"Sure, just ask the man and I'll pay for the gum along with these shoes," I said. Mark asked the clerk for a piece of gum and was shocked by his strange and hateful answer. "We don't have any gum."

At which Mark replied, "Yes, you do, it's right there"—pointing at the gum, which was no more than three feet from all of us.

"I don't have any gum for your kind of people," he said.

"What?" Mark asked, bewildered.

"Why so angry?" I asked the clerk.

"Just leave your shoes and get your asses out."

Mark interrupted, "I still want the gum."

I dropped the shoes on the counter, pushed Mark toward the door, and said, "Let's get the hell out of here."

"Why is he doing that? Why is he so mad at me?"

"He's not mad at you, Mark. Maybe he's just angry at himself—some people with twisted images of themselves are always angry. Just get out of their way. They're not worth it. This guy is unaware of his own ignorance. The world has passed him by and he wants to express his anger by being mean to a kid, a kid who already has more talent than he ever did or will have."

Turning back to the clerk as we leave the store, Mark called out so everyone in the store could hear: "Hey, man, stick the gum up your ass."

One of his remarkable attributes was Mark's ability to say the right thing at the right time, and to say it with reasoned and measured clarity. He was and would become more of a rebel as the discrimination continued. Years later, when Mark had achieved some fame as an outstanding athlete, many of these same people would fall all over themselves to shake his hand. I would always think about how Mark always seemed to have the right come-back.

The next weekend Mark and I drove all the way to Center-ville for shoes and a payment on the accordion. Kids, especially farm boys, drove anytime and anything they could from the time they could see over the steering wheel. Drivers' licenses came easy. But you didn't really need one. The process was simple.

When you reached the age of sixteen, you could stop a state trooper, even while he was having coffee at a local restaurant, and tell him you wanted a license. He would give you a form to fill out: name, address, age, and the length of time you'd already been driving. He then gave you a written test: maybe twenty questions about speed limits on Wisconsin roads (65 during the day…55 at night, etc.). And if you answered 18 of them correctly, you passed. Your license would show up in the mail in about six weeks. No photo, no behind-the-wheel test. For me, it was just his observation: "I like the way you hit the baseball." That was it. In two months, my license arrived in the mail.

On the way home from Centerville, we decided to treat ourselves and stopped for lunch at a drive-in. The jukebox was playing—Elvis, Jonny Ray, Patty Page. Mark and I each had a hamburger and a malt. Some guys from the local high school came in, recognized me and gave us some crap about our lousy football team. We were 0 and 3 and we were to win only one game that fall. I was a receiver, and in my mind, I thought that I was always open, but had no one to get the ball to me. We were awful and people would let us know—like we didn't know ourselves.

I would be happy to leave the cold fields of football and start basketball practice in early November. The resealed gym floor looked and smelled so good. And, I had my new shoes.

41

IN LATE OCTOBER I GOT MY OPPORTUNITY to play with the band at a Saturday night dance. It was a try-out. Happy wanted to see me play, so he and I drove to the dancehall in a little town of about 200 people called Pigeon River. We started playing at nine and would play until one in the morning. I did OK. I knew a few polkas pretty well, so I was given the lead to play two of my favorites. It was as much fun as scoring a touchdown.

During one of our two breaks, I recognized a pretty woman. She's that cheerleader from Milton Falls, a school in our conference, I thought. She walked over to the side of the stage where I was sitting, drinking some pop. "Hi, I'm Ann." I remembered her from basketball last winter, but had no idea how beautiful she was up close. Her reddish hair, green eyes, and that smile made my heart skip a beat or two. "Hi," I return.

"I love the way you play and was wondering if you could dance during the break."

There was always recorded music playing during the band's break, and right now, a waltz made popular by Patty Page was playing.

"I would like that."

I took her hand and led her onto the dance floor. Oh, my! This was nice. The dancing came easy, so I asked, "You live around here?"

"Half a mile from this spot," she said. "I love music," she continued. "I play the guitar, piano, and sing in the mixed choir in school. I have a confession to make; I've wanted to meet you ever since I saw you play ball against us last year. I know it sounds like I'm a traitor, can't help it. I came here tonight because my friend Jane saw the poster of your band. I had no idea that you played music, too."

All too soon, the break was over, and she said that they needed to leave. I made a request. "May I call you? Maybe we can go to a movie."

"Of course, call."

There are moments that change your life, right? At my age, a pretty girl could do that. It took several weeks, but I got the courage to call, and we planned to go to a movie.

Her mother answered the door. She was even more beautiful than Ann. Red hair, green eyes, and Ann's smile.

"Come in, Mike, I'm Mrs. Lee. Ann will be right down."

The living room was small, but it had a piano by the window, and there was a guitar in a stand beside it, a love seat, and two upholstered chairs. Ann appeared, looking more radiant than I remembered. Before I can stammer out some greeting, Mrs. Lee asks, "What movie are you two going to see tonight?"

"There's a new one that just started in Centerville—it's called *Giant*."

"I've heard good things about it," she says. "Before you two go, do you have time to listen to something Ann and I have been practicing?"

I nodded, Ann picked up the guitar, and Mrs. Lee began to play something on the piano. Wow, it was amazing. I had never seen this happen in a home before. They play a Jerome Kern song. It was so good; I didn't want the song to end.

As we were leaving, Mrs. Lee gave me five dollars. "This is to help with the gas, movie tickets, and snacks."

I would spend a great deal of time with Ann that year—dances after some ballgames, movies, and sometimes just to ride around or park and kiss after we ran out of things to say, and stop when our lips got sore. I learned about puppy love in the front seat of a '53 Chevy that year, but I was too frightened to engage with Ann. It's a hell of a thing when you can't connect with another because of fear.

Spring Prom. Even though I asked Ann to go with me to my prom, I didn't go, said goodbye over the phone, and never saw her again. Well, I did see her at ballgames—four more games—and I saw her some years later, from afar, playing the guitar and singing at the county fair. That was a long time ago, but sometimes I still remember Ann. I remember what I could have learned from her, about love and life, but I could not ... what if? Here was a girl who loved me and I was so stupid I couldn't see her. One of the smartest, sweetest people I ever met and I couldn't see her. My thoughts were defined by a toxic mix of shame and pride. Funny how pride might give you a moment's high and a lifetime of regret.

42

ALL THROUGH THAT SUMMER BETWEEN my sophomore and junior years, I still wanted nothing to do with girls. Pride is unhealthy for relationships. On the one hand, pride makes you think that you're special, but people are repulsed. But pride can also take you in another direction where it tells you that you're worthless, so you must do something to put yourself in a better light, just beyond reality, because you need acknowledgement from others.

In both cases, you're trying to get others to bolster you, to hold you up, and to define you. In the end, you become a jerk, because that's what people see in pride. Self-pride, sometimes sold as self-esteem, even obtained with hard work and the acquisition of possessions, simply creates unpleasant people. The owners of the lumber mill and the town sheriff were both disliked and made fun of, not because of their money or lack thereof, but because they had to tell us how important they were. And few cared. I guess that you can't be loved, if you're not lovely.

No more thoughts about romantic love. I would work to turn my focus on baseball, chores, music, and reading two books before school started, for no other reason than doing it. One book, which I just finished, was Salinger's *Catcher in the Rye*, recommended by Mr. Kennedy. That's a good example of pride—feeling sorry for yourself. Anyway, in my teenage situation, I thought the protagonist a little whining baby. Were we supposed to feel for him because he was looking for meaning inside his head? With all the advantages he had, he still wanted to end it all. Find himself? Really? Give me a break. I'd like to see him do my chores for a year; that would cure him of having time to feel so sorry for himself. The second book was Mark Twain's *The Adventures of Huckleberry Finn*, also recommended by Mr. Kennedy before he left. I would get to it soon.

I continued to play in the polka band all summer and into the fall. Ann never showed up again. I looked, but never saw her. I softened my sorrows with a very good Legion season, hitting over 400, and being selected to play on the state All-Star team. The groupies were there again, but now I saw them in a different light. With a continuing focus on myself and what I was doing, I lost my energy for others and for romance. I believed I was doing the right thing by winning games and playing well in the band. I did these things because I thought that others would like and respect me. But my world seemed a little less interesting without love.

I did love playing ball, as well as playing in the band, just because I liked the work and the art of it. Nevertheless, I continued to worry about what others thought. This feeling is what happens to you when you have no loved ones, or ones you love, to give you a sense of home.

Chores and field work were second nature now and, if not easier, certainly less mentally challenging. I had grown almost two inches since last summer and put on about ten pounds. With the start of my junior year, I felt more than ready to apply myself to the classroom and the football field.

Our football team was better this year, but we still lost more games than we won. I played some tailback, but mostly blocked for Tom, our starting tailback, who was as skilled as I, but a much better kicker. We did a lot of punting. Jerry, now a senior, was the best athlete in the school, but decided to skip football this year and concentrate on basketball. To be honest, I would have skipped football too, but what would people think?

The mid- and late 1950s were turbulent times, even in New Kassel. We got a small, but important, look at issues roiling the rest of the country like the Cold War and Civil Rights, but what I remember most about that entire school year and well into the next summer was the conflict between native people living on the reservation nearby, and the people in town, over enrolling Native children in New Kassel's public schools.

A few Indian parents who lived in town already sent their kids to public school, and one Indian student, a senior, was on the baseball team—a very good player. He played outfield and pitched. However, many more parents living on the reservation wanted to send their children to the schools in town. In a decade or so, when most of the reservations in the state started their gambling casinos, new schools would be built on the reservations and most of the children would return there. But for now, the issue was equality. Shrouded in racism, many still carried the belief that separate and "sort-of" equal was fine.

With real equity, however, many other issues could come to the surface, like appropriate curriculum, funding, busing, school board elections, and, perhaps the most contentious—how would

Indian children be enrolled and at what grade level? Many nine-
or ten-year-old Native students couldn't read. They had many
other skills, but their environment was lacking in most of the
ingredients needed for even limited success in the city's schools.

Enrolling the Native children would require the hiring of
some new teachers. How many students could one biology
teacher teach? If another was hired, how would he or she be
funded? Can you put children on a waiting list?

Since we have an obligation to teach all children in the
district but no legal responsibility to teach reservation children,
who should pay the additional cost? The Federal Government
had already paid for their schooling. The state said it would pay
so much per attending Native child, which amounted to a
fraction of the real cost, so the local districts would have to figure
it out.

43

THE SCHOOL BOARD MEETING THAT AUGUST was standing room
only. Several parents from the reservation were in attendance,
but they were far outnumbered by farmers, merchants, and
anyone else who could fit in the room and adjoining hallway.
Most of the early talk was about funding and maintaining
academic standards.

"They just can't handle the work," was a common refrain.

"We can't afford it," Some said.

And others, "We can't have quotas for non-native children.
Have them pass a test. If they can do the work, let them in. If not,
send them home. We can pay for the few who get in, but not for
all of them."

Then Cliff asked to speak. Of all the people in New Kassel, I
would least expect the town barber to say anything at this
meeting. Clifford got to his feet and thanked the board chair for
the opportunity to say a few words.

"The proper question, I think, is not about funding or legal
issues, but can we provide hope, inspiration, and role models for
children to whom we've denied things for as long as I can
remember? We have denied them any form of reasonable
education. We hide behind the law, which seems to work against
the very values of this country. Indians are also precluded by

prejudice from being employed in positions of responsibility. The outcome, of course, is a majority of their population is not educated, without skills, and unemployed. Just maybe we can turn some of this around by employing some Indians at the mill and admitting their children to our schools—and not on the basis of ability or passing a test, but because they are people who can enrich all of our lives."

Most of the people in the audience seem bewildered. Is Clifford saying that Indian children should be welcomed to school even if they can't do the work? Even if we have to share our few resources with them? He continued.

"If we do this right thing for these children and their parents, it will not only be for the benefit of the recipients of admission and employment, but for the benefit of all of our kids, who will grow up in an environment more favorable to hope and aspiration. I don't think that we can do anything else."

There is some polite clapping, nothing like an applause. But what Cliff and the rest of us need was an answer, so the president of the board, who is also the bank president, thanked Clifford and searched for a response.

"Balance, that's the rub, isn't it? For years, Washington has passed laws that have allowed society to practice racial discrimination against Native peoples, that's a fact. Are there any good reasons for the separation of Indians? Let's say that we, right here, decide to raise school taxes, prepare new curricula, and open our schools' doors and the mill to new workers. How many? Who will they replace? In other words, where do the lines get drawn, and who gets to draw them?

"Some people, perhaps like Clifford, always assume that they are the ones who get to decide. But what if I get to decide? Scary, eh? Do we endorse quotas?"

Catching his breath, he continues. "We cannot ask the government or this school board to pick winners and losers based upon race and history. Two wrongs do not make a right."

Then Frank gets up to challenge the president's comments. Frank is about eighty years old and sits beside his wife. He still works a dairy farm of about forty cows. I delivered firewood to their farm several times and had lunch and a nice talk with both of them last year. It occurs to me that Frank doesn't care what others think of him. He's grounded in his own character, and he's beautiful from the inside out.

"But we change history. It doesn't change by itself. My mother wasn't allowed to vote, but we changed that in 1920, and now my wife can. My farm was without electricity; we changed that. We had no hospital here; so, we changed that by forming a co-op. We can make our community better by including people different from ourselves. Hell, most of us right here are so different from each other, I wonder how we work and learn and live together. Each one of us makes each other better. En-so?"

People took the issues seriously and argued with reason and civility. This was the first of several board meetings on the subject.

The general story of those meetings was reported in the weekly paper and a summary of the procedures suggests that in late October, several Indians from the reservation attended, mostly to listen. The more they heard, the less likely they were to send their children to the public schools. As part of the on-going dialog between the school board and the Indian community, two teachers from the reservation school spent several days at the high school library to see how Indians were portrayed in the books used in history classes and for general student reading. They reported that almost all books painted Indians as savages or as people who were without will power. They could not find Indians portrayed as professionals, living in good communities, or serving their country in the military.

After reviewing the literature and history courses, they also found no mention of Native cultures before Columbus or of the many ways that Indians sustained the first European immigrants to North America. There was no record of the fact that many of our towns and cities have Indian names. Their culture dates back almost ten thousand years, and only four hundred years ago, they presided over at least ten million acres of what became the state of Wisconsin – another Indian word. The record from that time to now was nowhere to be found.

Thinking about the newspaper reports, I remember the cowboy movies we saw in Chicago. I believe that we invented the Indians in the way that we did, so we could play Cowboys and Indians forever, and never face the facts of what was stolen from them. Years later, I believed that our public policy decisions should help better the lives of Indians, just as they should for all people. If we really understood our own self-interest, we would work to have open housing, fair employment, and all of our public schools would be first-rate, with content emphasis on the liberal and civic arts.

Anyway, after issues of funding, the question most asked by members of the board concerned how the current books and courses of study could be altered to reflect a truer picture of Indian history and cultures.

The question was asked of the two Indian teachers who were evaluating materials and of a new history teacher who was just hired this past summer to teach world history, world literature, and to help coach basketball. He had just graduated the previous May from UW-Madison and was a native of Denver. He had played on the Badger's basketball team, never as a starter, but played in most games on a mediocre Big Ten team. He was darker than me, taller too, and the girls thought he was "dreamy." As a senior, I didn't have any classes with him, but thought he had a lot to offer on the basketball court.

Mr. Salto was his name. Carlos Salto. What a cool name. He was asked by our principal and the school board, along with the two Indian teachers, to make some recommendations about how Indian history and cultures might be incorporated into the high school courses of history and English. This was an interesting, and no doubt, political choice in addressing the issue. Two Indians and a Latino, little chance of success, but they gave it a try. Political power is always a function of connections and these three had few connections in town, on the board, or with the business community.

As it turned out, the three of them came up with a framework that, surprisingly, other teachers used. It presented a series of questions that all cultures had to answer, regardless of temporal and geographic location.

I would witness almost none of this, and I was the loser for it. Within five years of my graduation from high school, inaccurate books were beginning to be removed from the library, and new, more up-to-date ones purchased. History and Civics teachers took it upon themselves to incorporate culture questions in their classes, as well as new Indian history research in their thinking. And, the new Indian student/athletes led the basketball team to two conference championships in those five years.

In that time, so long ago, this work on race relations was trying to make school context more accurate, and it was all led by teachers. However, it was already clear to those who looked, that the divides among native people, town people, and farmers was wide and getting wider. And that wasn't all. All across the nation rifts between and among economic classes, education levels, and ethnic groups were also growing, or, at least, becoming more visible. Our basic problem was that we saw each other as liabilities and not assets; as subjects, and not as citizens. And above all, there seemed to exist in the land a deep existential fear—a fear of being disoriented in a landscape that was becoming ever more meaningless, leaving the individual feeling alone and separated from sustaining beliefs.

44

I REMEMBER A GENTLE, COLD RAIN falling. This is strange for November in Wisconsin. The temperature was below forty degrees and the rain felt heavy. Many of the drops were turning into large snowflakes. To be honest, I like days where the heavy drizzle slows the rush of life and gifts you with time unearned.

We are so accustomed to earning every second here. Twenty-four/seven/365—that's the dairy farmers' work year; it's their identity. Farmers love cold, drizzling rain. These days provide time to dream up meanings for their existence. There can't be too many of these days, however, or the cow madness strikes. This doesn't mean that the search for meaning is insincere, though. If you listen to the people of the land—not the corporate raiders—you will hear the wisdom of nature's law.

The discussions are still there today. The old generation dearly holds to them. And some fifty years later, I can often hear the words of John, who had been the kid on the farm next door and took over the management of the farm from his dad. When he turned sixty-five, John told me, "Back when you and I were kids, playing Legion ball, I had no idea that I would be an old man by the time I turned forty-five. I had the freedom to change my circumstances, which of course, I never did. Few of us do. On the other hand, I loved the days of cows and baseball—thought they would never end. Back then, I remember community members helping each other. Now everyone is too afraid to say anything. Maybe we don't help each other as much because we began to believe that the government would care for us and the children, and wouldn't you know it, families quickly laid down the sweet burden of parenting. Maybe because we were so poor, we had to depend on each other. I do think people helped people in their old communities, and the last place they'd look to for help was the government, especially the federal government. We appealed to local government. I mean local: neighborhood, ward, township, village, and sometimes the state."

Was John accurate? I can't say, but this is what John and others still believe. Back then, in the 1950s, the people of New Kassel talked and acted differently. We were a sharing community. Our hospital was a cooperative, owned by the farmers. We purchased machinery together, hay bailers, thrashing machines, silo fillers, hay rakes, and even seed corn. In many ways, we acted like socialists. There was pride in the land, the town, and even the person.

People were not as separated by wealth as they are today. Sure, some people were poor, in money, if not in spirit. This lack of material wealth left them with few choices. I think that the best thing about having "some essential or basic income" is that it allows you to make choices. In the fifties, these farmers voted Democratic, Eisenhower notwithstanding. Today it's hard to find a Democrat unless you go to Madison or Milwaukee. Why the change?

Why, indeed? The lies of Vietnam, the misplaced promises of the Great Society, the even bigger lies of weapons of mass destruction and the invasion of Iraq, the corruption of businesses and banks, and the resulting economic decline. The greed that grew out of our new and transparent values of hallucinating drugs, media addiction, materialism, sexuality, athleticism, and self-esteem, coupled with a lack of leadership, and the moral and behavioral scandals that hit every one of our institutions, from churches to businesses, from Congress to the White House. Most of all, many in the media have become complacent, believing that their job is to entertain or inculcate, unreflectively, the values of consumption without personal responsibility. They and perhaps, all of us, have slowly given up our moral authorship and governing partnership.

The pursuit of money, not the pursuit of truth, is what John and the others believe to be America's motto. It's hard to find citizens in the media or even in the White House, where a President stated that he was smart and proud of the fact that he could pay as few taxes as possible—understanding nothing about the nature of a republic and even less about virtue. Lincoln stated that the best framed and best administered governments are necessarily expensive. You get what you pay for. This is most true of education. We have paid dearly for our collective ignorance.

As I look at our society today, I see parents, communities, businesses, and even government officials who have given up on public schools, particularly when integration happened. Of course, we should have known better. You should not ask your children to do what you refuse to do. If we wanted an integrated society, we should have insisted on fair employment, open housing, and better infrastructures. Because of the behavior of the adults, the children believed that we were lying to them — and we were. We might still believe that education is the gate through which all children must pass if we expect a republic and market economy to prosper, but, we also seem to believe that schools and teachers are the only ones responsible when our children generally fail in scholarship and citizenship.

We forget that the gatekeepers to scholarship and citizenship are found beyond the school. This is the case because the gate is first and foremost the value that Americans place on intellectual activity, thoughtfulness, and civic engagement. If we stand divided, it is because we have broken our generational covenant.

In the end, it seems that our children are really not that important to us. Who are the poorest among us? Who have the poorest diets? Who are the most abused? Who have the most inadequate healthcare? In all cases, "children" would be the answer.

This condition was not created by schools. It was created by a general attitude, as well as by government officials, business, media, courts, and legislatures who didn't and still don't understand the purpose and integrity of the public schools. The fact of the matter; there is no shortcut to learning. It takes hard work, time, and most of all, a purpose that transcends the individual, and places first value on thoughtfulness and our democratic and market environments, outside of which there is little or no chance that we can be free.

You might say it is a given that "we are the land of the free and the home of the brave" and will always be. This is not a given. How free are we when we can't jog through our parks at night? How brave are we when we are afraid of fellow citizens?

There are a lot of similarities between now and the 1950s. The main difference, however, is that the '50's generation still understood that there was no free lunch. You worked, you saved, and you contributed to the larger community. We still had a universal draft, service to family, community, and nation were things you just did. In no way, however, was that a better time in which to live—just different. We had to deal with a new Red Scare, Joe McCarthy, racism, H-bomb tests, civil unrest, and many other issues. Nevertheless, we seemed to have more resiliency and sense of responsibility for self and the larger community. We often think that some "outside" force will destroy the republic—like the Russians, the Chinese, or even Mother Nature. Nope! The only thing that will destroy the republic is American ignorance. An ignorance of our identity as citizen--holder of the highest office in the land, together with a deep understanding that our republic is an ongoing argument over democratic values. That argument must be enlightened, civil, and steeped in the knowledge and tensions between freedom and equality; unity and diversity; common wealth and private wealth; and law and ethics.

45

By late February, we had the conference basketball championship in hand, and in March, found ourselves in the championship game of the central Wisconsin sectional tournament, one game from State, in Madison. There were no school classifications based on the size of the school back then. You simply had to play everyone, and we had the opportunity to play a school five times our size. They had an all-state forward and a front line of six-footers. Our tallest guy, Keith, was 6 foot 2. Their guards were both 5 foot 10, so we did measure up in the back court.

The game was played in the regional state college fieldhouse and every seat was filled with fans from the four participating schools.

We started strong and built a lead of ten points with only a minute left in the first half. Jerry scored 12 points while I contributed 11. In the third quarter, their all-state forward, Jim Spegelburger, took control of the game, both defensively and offensively. He scored ten points in the quarter and held me to two free throws. Jerry could do little better, scoring only five points, and at the beginning of the fourth quarter, we trailed 43 to 36.

We would lose the game, 55 to 47. To this day, fans who remember the game thought that we could have won and made our way to Madison. In my senior year, we would win the conference championship again, but would never be that close to going all the way to State.

Spring brought baseball and planting. We had a very good team, with good pitching and four of us hitting over 400, but, as with basketball, we missed the state tournament by one game.

Before summer vacation, I was elected president of our senior class, and had the opportunity to be a non-voting member of the school board. The board also hired me to take the school census. Using the records from the last few years, I needed to verify the number of children in each family and record all new births and the names of all students who would enroll in the several schools in the district.

Scheduling census trips in between my other activities of farm work and baseball, it took me from early June to August 15 to finish the work. That summer, I got to step inside every home that had pre-school children, and talk to every mother and many dads about all kinds of things, from the spelling of names, to the price of milk, to just how good our teams would be next year when I would be a senior. The school board paid me twenty-five dollars for the work.

There was an interesting mental awakening that occurred while visiting all these homes. Insight. What appeared from a distance as a single culture was exposed as a patchwork of dizzying variety and complex diversity. This all seems clearer once you are in the home and confronted with an assortment of new and different smells, sights, and sounds. Every home was a work in progress. Seeing these homes helped me better under-stand the creative imaginations of family and love.

Each home had its unique decor, sense of time, and objects of beauty. What amazed me was the way each home seemed locked in time. Change was not as important as harmony, and harmony was a way to ensure a continuing restoration of some image of by-gone perfection. In such a climate there is little concern for progress or development, for the inhabitances have given up the complexities of history and sustain the present and future through myths and ceremonies. It was like all of their institutions were churches, complete with dogma, doctrine, ceremonial escorts, and rituals. Within this context, I was, no doubt, seen as some important representative of the school, and even at my young age, given due respect. While there was much in their lives that seemed practical, their lives seemed to transcend the pragmatic and embrace a world of mystery where the here and now seemed clear enough, while the worlds of Madison, Milwaukee, Chicago, and other far-off places were as hallucinations.

I have to believe that the immigrants or newcomers, and the poor, have trouble creating a home. They live in places built by others and spend little time at rest there. The rich, on the other hand, can create their own homes and can choose to live there for a long time. If they can, the poor (farmers) make beauty and celebrate permanence with objects, stories, and special events. These things are personal and symbolic, and as important to the creation of meaning as anything the rich can do.

To most of the families I visited that summer, New Kassel was an abstraction. Their identity was related to the town, but it seemed that only their farm or the region around their house or street was real. There were many learnings and stories that came from my happy work that summer. Some were funny, like the day I drove into a neighbor's driveway and finding no one around the house, walked toward the barn. On the far side of the barn, by the fence in the cow pasture, I saw Mrs. Miller taking a bath in the cows' drinking tank.

As I approached, she screamed, "Don't come any closer!"

"I'm taking the school census," I said.

"Come back later, and don't tell anyone, Mike."

"OK," I said, "I will try, See you later."

Most memories, of course, came from meeting and talking to people who had seen me play ball and suggested how their lives were tied to the sports seasons, not just watching baseball or basketball, but riding emotional highs and lows depending on the flow of the season. For the first time, I listened to adults talk about me and high school sports like it was not only a fun activity to attend, but as an important and defining moment of their week.

High school athletics was the only show in town, and today, I see it as true and profoundly troubling. Baseball was not just about hitting a baseball; it was about ubiquitous values and the community. At one level, you could see it in the architecture of our high school. If values are related to allocations of resources, certainly the gym was the most imposing structure on campus. And while the lumber mill, and some of the taverns, stores, and farms were impressive, the baseball diamond, park, and picnic areas were far more beautiful. There may have been pride in the town, but even more pride in the aesthetic of sports.

My hunch is that without the high school and high school athletics, the town would have had to create a new identity. The school was the community anchor. It's what brought people together, physically for a Friday evening, and spiritually for a lifetime. I never knew this little fact about America then, now I see it in every part of the nation. But it's very different today.

As our public pride and faith in public education atrophied over the years, so too the defining qualities of community and of sport. High school athletics has morphed into more of a show-case where stars develop their superman personas. The community doesn't attend high school games like they did, unless their team is in a championship game. Through TV, athletic attention has shifted to money and the power of the NFL, NBA, and the NCAA. Our modern teams play in nothing less than cathedrals where players are worshipped and corporate symbols are branded into the minds of people.

Within this new corporate context, identity shifted from "home team," with all its corny and naïve practices of support, to professional identities, or brand name, covered with offensive odors of greed and celebrity. In 1957, Pee Wee Reese's salary, as a Hall of Fame shortstop, was $14,000. Today, even an average major league shortstop might make $4 million. But more importantly, the game in 1957 was more exciting, more thoughtful, more 'hometown,' and far less expensive to attend. Today, it is difficult for a family to afford to attend a major league baseball game.

In most cases, the money that fills the pockets of the owners and used to build and maintain the cathedrals of sport, come, in no small way, from taxpayers. We are unreflectively willing to give entitlements to the few to entertain and maintain the notion of city pride. How wonderful it would be to show such pride in education, healthcare, and quality infrastructures for the many.

The rationale for this innocent and dangerous priority is a credulous notion that a sport stadium will produce more revenue for the city than quality education, healthcare, and art.

46

SEPTEMBER PRESENTED A LANDSCAPE with vibrant colors and an incredible busy but manageable agenda. Mark would start his sophomore year and I my senior. Next spring, we would both be starting on the high school baseball team, and he would lead the Jr. Varsity in basketball to an 18-and-2 season. By then, a deeper understanding of school allowed me to slow down time, such that I was able to see events more clearly. It was like the way a good hitter, in baseball, can slow down a pitch in his mind to the point where he can see the stiches on the ball.

I was also getting more interested in theories and principles, and less attentive to events. This ability was great in math class, but it also caused me to move away from people. It was becoming more difficult to have personal relationships with others. I was destroying the quality of living while becoming more able to explain human relationships to myself and others.

Throughout the year, I fell in love a few times, but in all cases, with perhaps one exception, I would only experience the theory and not the thrill of love, because the idea of love seemed more interesting than the person.

The other thing I theorized about was time. I could wait for love or whatever, because for me, time transcended the individual and focused on the everlasting. I would abuse time, believing that in me, it would go on forever. Time didn't matter. The work didn't matter. I had time to do it all. I would outlast it all. My behavior was controlled by my made-up and unprovable time theories and by the stories I learned in books and movies about eternal heroes. Be good, don't get close, and kill your emotions, except when you are alone with your music, your story, and your affections. Then you can laugh or even cry if you want. No one will care. I thought all good things would eventually come to me, not understanding that the future really does leave footprints in the present. You will be loved the way you love. You will be treated the way you treat others. You will die the way you lived. And so it goes.

At the first senior class meeting, early in September, the class voted to leave a gift for the school. After about a half-hour debate, there was enough agreement around an idea to buy a complete set of atlases for the school library. The National Geographic Society provided us information on what materials would be appropriate for high school students and adults, and we agreed to purchase ten reference atlases. For me, this would be the first of many engagements with the Society and in over forty years, I have been the gainer in every case.

My fall agenda was full with one-act-play competition, the state FFA parliamentary procedure contest, football where I was playing offensive end and defensive safety, and, of course, classes. As a senior, I was taking physics, advanced algebra, Latin, American government, and English. I spent a great deal of time in the agriculture building as well. As a member of FFA and still learning about the complexities of farming—particularly the financing of a business that professed to be a way of life—I continued to be fascinated by just how much a farmer had to know, do, and be. And, then, there were the farm chores and the work of sometimes helping Mark prepare meals and keep a house clean.

She came up to me after the class meeting. Sarah. We've been friends since our freshman year, but as she approached, I saw her differently. Wow, she's a woman, I thought. Beautiful. Black hair and eyes that were a rich blend of emerald and gray. She had an athlete's body—powerful, graceful, and energetic.

"Any chance we can talk about the class gift? I love maps and would like to help research our needs for the library."

"If we can find some time in the next few days, we can do that," I reply.

"Would next Monday, after chores, work for you? I could come over to your house at 7:30."

In situations like this, I'm never sure if the beauty of the woman or the task at hand is the motivation for engagement. Anyway, Monday came, and right after chores, I got cleaned up and drove over to Sarah's house.

SARAH AND HER FAMILY LIVED ON THE edge of town, in a neighborhood of poverty. The block on which she lived was an area of deeper poverty. There were several Indian families living there, and the poverty was palpable. Sarah's father was Irish and her mother Sioux. In this part of the state, dominated by the Menominee people, she had the worst of two worlds: being Irish in a German town, and being Sioux in a Menominee neighborhood. The heritage of her genes made her breathtakingly beautiful with mental sensibilities observable in only a very few people.

I knocked on her door just after the last light of twilight was fading, and in that soft glow, the place seemed, well, it seemed welcoming.

"Hi, I'm here to see Sarah." I nervously said to Mr. Kelly. He was about forty-five, I would say, but looked about sixty. He had a two-day growth on his face and looked like he had just returned from work at the lumber mill, with an intermediate stop at the tavern.

"Sarah's in her room." He called out in a loud and very gravelly voice.

"Sarah, there's some guy here to see you." He turned and walked into the kitchen without saying a word to me.

Sarah came half-running out of her room, looking even more beautiful than she had earlier today.

"Let's talk in the living room," she said.

We proceeded into the living room, sat together on the couch, and looked at each other for a long minute, and in that moment, I forgot what I came here for.

"Is your mother home?" I asked.

"She's with her people, who live just off the reservation. She may be back later."

Her people? I thought it was a strange way of describing the location of your mother. As far as I knew, there was only one other Sioux family in the county, and they lived in isolation just off the Menomonee Reservation. Maybe that's where her mother was. Sarah saw a much more complex world than the generalities about Indian and white could ever define. I thought my world was divided; hers was atomized.

We worked on the library project for about thirty minutes, picking out the atlases we believed would enhance our school library. Our constructed list would be ready to put before the senior class.

As I got up to leave, I felt the need to give Sarah a hug. As I opened my arms to embrace her, she extended to me a soft embrace that melted us into one another. On her part, there was no standing back with her body, the way girls hug at school or even on a date. This was a real hug from one of the prettiest of them all.

"Bye," I say and quickly tried to leave, still feeling her arms holding me.

"Good-bye. See you tomorrow."

She was still holding my hand and I paused. Perhaps, for the first time in my life, I realized that I love to hug and be hugged. In fact, I don't remember ever being hugged before. I was painfully aware that no long embrace has ever been part of my life. It was like being conscious to a human touch. It felt good. It was good. I wondered, however, if the experience was a singular event or something that could be realized again and again.

As you grow and mature, you wonder if every experience is unique. Perhaps, but I wanted to believe that this experience could be repeated. Experience is contextual within time and place, and context is never so much created as discovered or revealed. But more, it is a one-time thing—never again.

In that time and place, Sarah and I looked at each other and were able to shut out the world and simply be together, alone.

"Your dad was so quiet."

"He's in the basement, working on something."

"And your mother? Will she be back soon?"

"She's been on and off the reservation for several weeks now."

"Why?"

"You've seen my father? He's simply gone, too. I would be with my mother, but I really want to finish school here. Maybe even go to college. I try to make it through each day—learning, thinking, and hoping for a better future. What you see here, this house, these conditions, is not me."

Not knowing what to say, I repeated myself. "Will your mother come back?"

"I really don't know; she wants to be with her people. They are not my people, but my father's not my people either. I get dizzy thinking about it."

I squeezed her hand and lingered a little, etching this moment into my mind.

I finally start to leave and get into my car. We were from different worlds—not of class or ability, but of perception. Her perception came from a history of non-identity. Not Indian, not European, not American. She saw herself as fitting nowhere. For a moment, we could escape into each other, but the noise of the world is relentless. I had Uncle's stories. She had…I don't know what she had. Her Native histories seemed far too sad to embrace, and her stories of the Irish in America didn't play much better. If all you have is the future, you enter it rudderless.

Sarah's future, like mine, would be shaped by our perceptions of our past stories, the stories of how and why our families and personal lives mix with the larger narrative of our society.

There would be times throughout my own life when I would feel alone, out of touch with any family, and homeless even within my own house. In this land I call "my land," many times, I couldn't find a home. I think I understood Sarah, but did I? Could I?

My mind is so full of emotions that I didn't remember the drive home. I felt so good thinking about her and about seeing her tomorrow and perhaps even falling in love. But I would never see Sarah again. I was told that her mother took her back to the reservation. I always believed she didn't have a choice. She was gone.

Gone indeed. She never came back to high school. I did drive out to the reservation the next week to see her, but was told she was gone from there, too. End of story. Well, not altogether. Over the years, I constructed a vision of love and friendship that colored my relationships with women, simply because no real person can withstand the perfectibility of one's imagination. Again, I turned to what was left, my work, my game, my studies, and to a new desire of getting away from there.

Autumn has come to my habitat,
And the countryside is wrapped in brilliant hues of red and gold.
In this place and at this time,
It seems easier to think of you, and of love.
I know the beauty of fall is only an interlude,
Played against a louder symphony.
As our love is an interlude,
Played against the noise of life.
Yet both are the handiwork of God,
Transcending time and giving witness,
To the immortality of beauty.

47

THE HOMECOMING BONFIRE SEEMED particularly big and warm. It had turned cold by early October and tonight the cold wind carried sparks high into the night sky. Some snow flurries made acquaintance with my face, and I knew that the cold would be a player at tomorrow's game. But there was the homecoming dance after the game and perhaps, after three weeks, I could possibly dismiss Sarah from my mind as I had from reality.

We lost the game. As we left the field, alumni gave us a hard time, some coming right down to the locker room to suggest that we were of a different gender. Somehow, it didn't seem to matter. Even Happy's familiar comment, "You guys are just too nice to beat anyone," didn't seem to stick.

After showering and putting on my street clothes, I reluctantly went up to the gym to see if anyone was in a better mood there. What was clear, perhaps for the first time, was the fact that most students didn't seem to care that much about the outcome of the game. We were not going to win a championship anyway, so relax and dance. I had trouble with that attitude, but little energy to fight it now.

"Jane, care to dance?"

"Sure," she said, so I took her hand and we walked to the middle of the gym floor. I always felt comfortable here. Perhaps because we're on the basketball court. I loved that feeling. Jane was one of my best friends and easy to talk to. She was a buddy.

"Too bad about Sarah."

"Yes, I saw her just before she went to visit her mother. Now she's gone, too. I didn't know I would miss her so much, but I do."

"Why did she leave?"

"I don't know, Jane. Perhaps some of us simply can't stomach the place we're in and leave, even when loved. I guess a person has to be told that they are loved. I don't know."

"Let's talk about something else tonight and enjoy the dance," she said.

Mostly we talked about our futures. She was going to be a nurse. I had no idea. The Air Force looked good, but so did college. I just knew that I couldn't stay here.

"Can you drive me home?"

"Sorry … No … Happy took the car after the game. I was going to catch a ride with someone else."

"Well, I'm sure Sandy and Jim can take us both home. We'll just jump in the back seat."

On the ride home, Jane got way too friendly. First, she removed her shoes and put her feet and legs over my lap. Then she gave me a hug and kissed my neck. Jim seemed to already have plans to park with Sandy, so Jane said, "Let's go for a moonlight ride." After a few more kisses, her dress was up around her waist and we continued to touch and kiss each other in ways that were different from anything I had done before; different but thrilling.

By the time we arrived at my house, I was in that joyful pain that comes when you're young and happy. As I got out of the car, Jane expressed interest in the idea that we should see more of each other. There would only be a few dates, movies, and malts, and some more intense kissing and petting.

I lost interest before Christmas and had only two dates the rest of the winter and spring; both were with girls from other schools. Mostly basketball and then baseball kept my interest, along with my two favorite classes, Math and American Government.

We won the conference championship in basketball but could not make it out of our regional tournament. Baseball, however, was different. We did go to the state tournament where major league scouts would select two of us from New Kassel for try-outs. Our pitcher, Gene, was the complete ball player with all the necessary skills—throwing, hitting, fielding, running—was taken first by the Milwaukee Braves, and three years later, was ready to move up to the majors as a third basemen, to eventually replace Eddie Mathews. Sadly, Gene was killed in a deer hunting accident that very year.

I received a tryout opportunity from the Cleveland Indians, .586 batting average, with good speed and arm, but would not make it through the first summer in the minors. My time playing within the Cleveland system, in Iowa, lasted just over one month. Every player seemed better than me. Coach also moved me from shortstop to second base, and the move effected my whole attitude about the game and about myself. The manager and I both agreed that professional baseball was perhaps beyond my skill level. I ended up back home, and by August, started playing again with the home-talent team.

My senior year in high school and the following summer passed at lightning speed. Throughout the year, each game we played punctuated the fact that this would be the last time we would play Centerville or Fort Amherst. I would seldom go with the gang for hamburgers and malts after a game. Never would I kiss Sarah or Jane or Ann again, or run home from the gym to the farm after football practice. I would never have another chance to play in the minors. I could list these nevers but had no sense of the things that I could do tomorrow.

Leaving high school was a melancholy time for me. The mix of joy and sadness seemed altogether true. Graduation was, and is, like life. If you're lucky, you learn prudence and sacrifice. Sacrifice is simply the understanding that ease and wants are given up today for better ease and enjoyment later. The farm work showed me the need to study and become as knowledgeable as possible about the world around us. It taught me that any knowledge you study is like walking into the ocean, it gets deeper the farther you walk.

48

WE WERE NOW WELL INTO AUGUST and I had no idea of what fall would bring—college, army, farming? Mama was back home since May, and things seems to be going fine with the farm work, with my relationships at home and with neighbors, and with my sense of self. I just needed to make a decision about the coming year. At about 11:30 one morning in mid-August, a recruiter from a small liberal arts college in Wisconsin showed up at the farm. Mama welcomed him into the house for lunch and to discuss college possibilities. I always thought I would go to college, and now the issue was put right before us.

"We've been following you this past year and know that you graduated third in your class. You're good in three major sports too. We would love to have you on our campus next month. Mike, do you have any specific plans for college?" Mr. Bennett asked.

"I would like to attend a college, but really haven't thought much about it or made plans for next year. And there are issues like paying tuition and helping with the chores."

"Tuition is $700 a year, but that does not include your books, room, and all your meals," he said.

It might as well be $7,000, I thought.

"We would also offer you a kitchen job at our main cafeteria, and we have Air Force ROTC, which would cover your tuition.

This would take care of most of your financial issues, but you and your mom would have to solve the work issue on the farm."

I thought a minute about college and the opportunity represented by the recruiter, and also about Mama, Happy, and Mark with two more years left in high school. To this day, I wished that I had talked to him about his feelings of staying there alone and about his plans for college and the future. But I didn't and have regretted it all these years since. It was a cowardly decision that Mama and I made. No, that I made and it served to make Mark bitter and to alienate us through our adult lives.

The recruiter left after lunch. He left information and forms to be filled out and mailed to the college if we were interested. After cleaning off the table, and with hesitation, I asked: "Ma, can we talk not about college, but ... about us?"

"What?"

"Can you tell me what has been going on these last few years? Now that I'm about to leave, can you tell me why we moved here in the first place? And once here, why did you leave us? Knowing that we were only going to spend a few months together over the last four years. I would like to know why and what you were thinking and have you been doing?"

"That is not your concern, but I will tell you what I think you need to know.

"Our lives in Chicago were unacceptable. I hated that I had to work two jobs—menial jobs that had no future. I didn't like some of the people I worked for and the low expectations they had for me. I needed to get out of there, and you two needed it more. I understood your anger with me and our situation, still do. I did things in the only ways open to me. I did leave the farm and go back to Chicago to pay for things that we needed. Do you know how close we were to being homeless?"

I was hoping she would stop, but she didn't. "You think life here was hard? You don't know hard."

"But…" I tried to break in.

"I feel as guilty as you feel angry. But we can work to make this better, or we can go our separate ways. We are both too tired to carry this conversation any further. "

Mama stopped talking, but my mind would not rest. The thing about life is you get to live it, and it is consumed in that living, in the performance. What I experienced was gone; consumed, except for the memory; and what I continue to learn by remembering. Remembering can set you free, but only if the reminiscence is not in anger.

I also hold to a different story. Since that day, I have worked to balance the memories of anger or disappointment with those of joy, but the mind is a ferocious debater, so the arguments continue. I missed out on the 'we' experience with my birth family, the feeling you can share everything with a special person or persons. People who hold respect and appreciation for you, and, perhaps, even rely on you.

"I really want to go," I finally say, almost like someone else was using my voice. And that was that. We would talk, years later, but it would be empty words, devoid of meaning and satisfaction. I was left to mythologize, again and again.

Now, after four years of learning what the land could teach, I was about to 'pass on' or depart my present life. Moving through time and place, I wonder what I will keep from this present life? What will I throw away? What will I know to build anew? Tacitly or explicitly, these are the three questions of life that must be addressed, or dying and rebirth stop, suspending us in a continuing and innocent childhood. This, above all, is what I took away with me.

Within an hour, over dishes, the decision was made. I was to be on my way to college. In three weeks, I would be standing alone by the side of the road, one bag in tow, waiting for the Greyhound bus that would take me to a new life and into my future. As the countryside of hills, forest, and dairy farms rolled by, it became clear that I couldn't find or create a home here. Looking out of the bus window, I could see that in the time and space of a hundred miles, I would be out of this town and off the farm. After four years I had graduated from both school and land. I meant to leave it all behind, but I took volumes away with me that day so long ago.

Now, as I continue my journey on this little country road to visit that old friend, I realize that I never made it out of here spiritually or psychologically—the memory chases me still.

So often now my thoughts drift back to that landscape,
The beauty of the time, work, and the sunlit pastures,
Echo feelings of joy and pain across my consciousness.
I'm alone now, in spirit, in love,
And the world seems a little colder,
Except when my thoughts drift back.
The joy I experience in dreaming,
Is matched only by the constant pain of separation.